THAT LONES

by

Melissa Lee-Houghton

*You can't really
lose

Lov

Melissa* 💚

Edition 078/500

MORBID BOOKS

A limited edition of
500 numbers copies of
That Lonesome Valley by Melissa Lee-Houghton

Published in Great Britain by Morbid Books

Distributed in the UK and Europe by Central Books

Cover image by Shane Wheatcroft
Layout design by Karolina Grzelak

Join the Temple of Surrealist Literature
patreon.com/morbidbooks
morbidbooks.net

ISBN 978-0-9956450-8-0

Also by Melissa Lee-Houghton

A Body Made of You (Penned in the Margins, 2011)
Beautiful Girls (Penned in the Margins, 2013)
Sunshine (Penned in the Margins, 2016)
Cumshot in D Minor (Offord Road Books, 2017)
The Faithful Look Away (Rough Trade Editions, 2018)

*"There's something inside me
that just won't let me be."*
– Elmore James, Something Inside of Me

PART I

MORGAN

One *Born Under A Bad Sign*

After two unforgiving days suffering an acute sense of worthlessness that wasn't erased when I last quit heroin, I tell her about the *blue hour*. I tell her, "it's the hour artists and poets favour, before twilight or dawn, when the light changes and is best." Her mouth forms a delighted O; she is a poet and yet such names for things she forsakes from her memory in favour of the affect or sensation their occurrence brings. Any inessential information or stimulus she casts out and seems to hold onto only what her heart understands. Hers is a rare and singular compulsion, to submit to nothing but her own will. And therein we understand each other.

I deposit my delightful sweetheart at The Three Compasses and implore her to choose a seat. She unhesitantly opts for a particularly dark booth. The place is slightly odious and stinks of a barely concealed sewage problem and I realise this is the most inappropriate setting for such a creature as her to exist. I'll be gone half an hour but I'm pained by the thought of leaving her in the midst of East London decrepitude in her purple housewife dress with her immaculately knotted hair. The helpless-seeming, shoulderless bartender pulls her a pint of craft cider and she sits and watches the bubbles rise in the honey-tinted liquor as though her world is all impulse, nimbus and libido entwined.

Buprenorphine is a drug that blocks heroin and acts as a substitute for it. I've been taking it for years as a chronic addict, intermittently adopting a part-time approach to heroin; when I met her the heroin was pared back to one or two days a week, with a two-day switchover to the inadequate opiate substitute, never experienced without a concurrent, overcast mood of mediocre rainstorms and excessive sweat. To be taken orally, though I choose to crush and snort it as white powder, so that I manage to abuse the cure to my drug abuse.

The day after the night I met Florence, when she had drunk four bottles of wine along with three or four grams of London cocaine, her hangover was so delicate and pitiful I helped her smoke heroin off my best bacofoil to lessen her pain. I realised I was so unwilling to see her suffer I could bring about suffering for her. My usual two days on heroin became two weeks and I refused to let her score, but her appetite equalled mine and so we shot to a halt in the middle of our lives and believed fully in immersing ourselves in a guiltless version of existing. She was keen to submit to the outmanoeuvring of her inculpable misery. She swore to me each day she had never been loved properly. She held hands with the love-pathologised addiction since she'd been good and hooked before, sometime in her teens and later, in her twenties. She doesn't blame me or regret the digression now she's straight – she says, "we're in this together," whenever our falling-in period of stoned bliss is mentioned. Some days I feel twinges of remorse for re-acquainting her with her favourite drug, but then, those two weeks she experienced a peacefulness I doubt she'd ever known, from the way she described her unbearable states of mind in the year leading up to the night we reached the clean-cut start-point of the other, and we fell in a new kind of love. I am unconvinced by love's universality, but I am utterly convinced by our unique variation of pangs, orgasms and panic that typified our initial first-flush.

I fumble-stumble into the street groping for my cigarette as Van Morrison's Brown Eyed Girl kicks in on the predictable sticky, black jukebox and go to score from a man my age, mid-thirties, who chooses to live in the cockroach-infested hostel I lived in for a time through lack of choice, ruminating over the dream I had the previous night about Argentina, whose palimpsest skyline of skyscrapers I despised and cowered beneath. I sweat heavily into my oatmeal coloured shirt as the sun sinks idly, but still

gloats at my poor sight until it's a squint – I think of her sitting in her often irremediable reverie, and I consciously re-imagine the guitar solo for Hot Burrito 2 by The Flying Burrito Brothers so the band can cover it for the next gig, but the notes don't hold together in my head; they don't even waver or float away, they stick in my nose and throat. It's hard to climb into thought safely when all I want is heroin and Her. She's thinking of me, I know it, greedily. I'm doing what I must do and have ever committed to, imagining all the ways the whole world shifted and changed decisively when mine collided with the imperfect, nimbus-warped vision of hers. Utterly wanted. So utterly wanted.

*

"Fame...is making my shit itch," she murmurs at three in the morning while I exhale the rich, pescatarian blood-clot smoke she just exhaled into my tightly-seized mouth. I think of the anti-histamines I forgot to buy and notice several patches of raised, raw skin where the scratching has gotten the better of her. She is too sensitive to gazes and immediately shudders and asks me what part of her I am staring at and the insistent query she too often reverts to at times of insecurity, "what's wrong with me?" relieves her anxiety via her slightly dehydrated mouth with barely a phoneme to aid my translation. She begins to growl; the growls often turn in her sleep to the sounds of a small mammal in the throes of bottoming out through pain.

I look past her, out across the Downs at this autumnal cot-death sky, but can't disband the compulsive melancholic reaction to all post-midnight, deepest-darkest night skies which have been responsible for too many silent and lonely bongo-head digressions from our star-happy and enviable, pure-sexual-love-enhanced twenty-four-hour surreptitious daydreams. Her black mesh baby-doll rises gallantly over her milky buttock and hip almost on cue with the corresponding urge to see it, as she scoots up to embark on a perilous journey to the other side of the room to find her pink tiger-striped clipper lighter in a bid to pretend not to fully comprehend my very exacting madness and pedantry in the fact of such private concerns as whether time is a construct which helps the unintelligent make plans they cannot fulfil full-heartedly. I hear her flick the lighter several times as the travellers down the street cackle and throw Kestrel cans into the park directly adjacent from the front door. Any other person may think it wise to draw her back in and allow her to feel wanted and yet, her emotional discombobulation is not my responsibility, just as mine is not hers, and the madness we inhabit together is an exquisite joy to abuse; we both have eyes channelling the light and dark into our heads and see identical visions of all things opening up like tulips in the morning, or her pussy, or her mouth as she moves to suck on my bottom lip with a tension around the eyes which visually describes rapture. I am too much for her and she raises my pulse so hard I sometimes crush us both under the weight of her inhalations and start to hyperventilate.

*

This morning we woke and I mentioned staring at the printed photograph on the wall in the empty flat we're staying in. I asked Florence, "what's that picture above the cats?" She replied, "a cat. Can't you see it? Its arm is poking out from an armchair. It's a kitten, sleeping." I responded, incredulous, "but I saw it as a galaxy, next to a planet, clouds of dust, stars..." "O," she cried out. "O, now I see it! Stars! I never saw that before. I saw a boring old cat, and now I can never un-see the planet and the galaxy. My God. How did I not see that until now? I wish I had your eyes."

"I'm blind," I mumbled. "I love your eyes," she whispered. "I love your eyes, your chest, your nipples (this one is my favourite nipple), I love your arms, your broad shoulders, your tan, your skin, the crooks of your arms, your veins, your head, your temples, your nose, your eyelashes, your curly hair, your belly, your abdominal scar, your pubis. Please can I touch you here? Can this part be mine? And here and here and here...?"

She didn't mention my legs.

The first time we were going to have sex I had to stop and I buried my head against her shoulder and tried to tell her about my legs. She kissed my head and said, "There's no rush, when you're ready." She stroked my head; she unzipped my trousers, but they've not been further than my very upper thighs in all the time we've been together. Now it's been so long she's afraid for me to tell her how they got smashed up. Why one is longer than the other. She asked me if they were that way from birth but they weren't and I lied. It's not going to make her feel better for her to know. She'll have more nightmares.

*

In three months we had three lapses. Once, after a fifty-hour conversation with myself about the cravings I had for heroin, I managed not to give in. I knew I could give in to it and I knew she'd agree unhesitatingly, though her argument against was also strong. She spoke of reality and I smiled. We wanted the antidote to such a concept, and it works. It works like snorting a dream and becoming ether. The last two lapses were hers, her longing, and her request, and I didn't say no because I knew her pain would be soothed.

The first time I held the lighter while she chased. I had to do it for the first week, perhaps. I had to tell her, "chase, that's it." I told her she was a good girl. If she did a really good chase on her own she would show me the unstreaked, unburnt foil and I would tell her she did really well. I've never injected but she has and knows how to. She wouldn't come back, and I'd be gone for good. We manage the entanglement of our precarious desires quite effortlessly. It sometimes becomes quickly irretrievable at moments of acute pain. Our pain is now one organ. If a part gets bruised or damaged we speak it together until neither of us can feel anything.

And that first day, she laid back on my bed and she asked me to lie with her. I didn't. She played with my hand, lying on the bed in her Sunday dress and white blouse, and she laid back and gouched on her own while I tried to roll an endless cigarette, never completing the task. I gave her a rocket ice lolly. She said it was the best thing she'd ever tasted. She couldn't eat it, the red slush just ran down her hands while she sat on my bed with a look of such peacefulness it felt as though my damage and her damage just tore up their tenancy agreement and walked out, leaving us penniless, leaving us alone, expecting us to care.

It's terrifying, having something to lose.

Before her I pawned the lot. It was as though the door shielding my life from an external hell was losing all its bolts and screws and had eventually slammed away from its hinges and into a netherworld and nothing could stop the rain and wind beating in.

In hindsight, I see she was intangibly present before I met her. I wondered why I went on and accepted suffering lame-headed and dumb-shouldered for as long as my lifespan, then the minute we'd done our fourth line and I looked at her as she shuddered in the cold slightly, put the heater on and made her coffee, I thought, "I have to thread her through myself, somehow."

A drug withdrawal is a period of loss, a bereavement; you end it, it dies, you grieve painfully and wish to have your love object back, but the love object becomes a shimmering fantasy, over a cliff edge, away. Every time we started we stopped, but every time we stopped we wanted to begin again, and we did, and we couldn't stop flying over the edge looking for the out-of-reach thing. We had one another, but it was as though the drug was enhanced by the possessing of one another, and there was no more need for it to blot out, but to explore, entrance, and we developed our love alongside our sweet opiate tooth.

*

I was born by a river, next to a railway line, and I've been living by railway lines ever since – not by choice. Railway lines map my geographical dependency on being midway between no place and no place. We lived by the railway line. When she came to me we walked down to Seven Sisters to the ATM to score and she said the hackles on her neck pricked up. She said she'd been so many places but none more prone to that vigilant tingle you get when you sense yourself being followed, watched, watched and followed or following the trail of something that might lead you to the ravine. I watch her sometimes walk towards me where we meet midway between no place and no place and she looks like she is being watched, being followed and watched, aware of being followed. We don't ditch that shadow.

*

I come in from the cold, ditch the clean trousers and shirt to score, get my hat on and turn my collar up, come back dripping with sweat. I have to look like no person. She is always waiting on the bed, her knees hunched up or laid out like a cat waiting for its owner to come home, two pats of foil laid out on newspapers folded in half. I make the tubes on a knife sharpener, cut them with paper scissors. The tubes are the gold at the end of the rainbow, always a better hit than the preceding bag. She wears a pink sheer nightgown with rips and safety pins to hold it together, or a black mesh babydoll with her tits pushed out, or a white lace camisole, see-through and down to her ass, and I take my place at the hilt of the bed while she shuffles down and we hit all the lighters to see which two have the biggest flame. I have to pile her bag onto the foil and fashion the channel for her to chase – if it's too close to the edge she complains. I have been doing this for years but she can only use the channel for the first half bag and then she says her foil starts to look Pollock. If she chases a good line she says, "look, I did it clean this time, do I win ten points? Am I a good girl?" I tell her she's a good girl. She beams and flicks the flint. She inhales and drops her head back into her shoulders, her face upturned to the sky and her eyes closed, momentarily absent then totally there.

*

He hits her up for £700 for the kid. She pays and coughs. She runs out of words, no vocalisation of anguish worth uttering in such circumstances as having been made homeless after being forced to live in her husband's attic for a year, cold through winter and colder in summer when he walked with his new piece in the woods with her dog, hand in hand, sun setting, everything rising over her head, the kid asking where she's gone. At that moment she was asking where she'd gone, she was bereft, penniless, inexcusably deadened by grief. Now she says she's glad she's just an addict. She was told she was so many things before, and people wanted her to be so many things and inhabit so many identities and fantasies, but now she is just an addict, just one simple thing.

I send her out for milk. We drink tea as the alcoholism she was running towards doesn't suit the smack. It makes her vomit more, turns her woozy in the afternoon and daydreaming all night with stomach ache and dehydration. She says she's done with that, and the cocaine, and the running, and the lonely bars, the hitting-on, the regular assaults against her nature, her sexuality. She fills places up; you can't get away from it; with her I sense it everywhere I go, dicks dripping with shameful urges, and she's too alive now, always has been.

I tell her the shop's just round the corner at the end of the street leading onto the main road. I tell her not to talk to strangers or weirdos as I always do. She clutches her handbag and walks in the white cowboy boots we picked up for £3 in Dalston. I think of how impossible it is not to notice her if you're selling, buying or waiting. It sometimes feels like the world is waiting for her to walk into it and drown in the air. She almost hyperventilates in her sleep, like she's dreaming inside a balloon and the air is closing up like a wound and her mouth is the wound and the lungs start to crackle then she wakes for a fix and I don't always let her. You can't cane it every hour. I know she never knows when to stop, and neither did I until I met her and had to let her know when to stop.

An hour passes and I call and call again and nothing from her. She's gone. Dead, murdered, run down or lost. I feel the absence; her dress is not her dress now but a white flag crumpled on the floor. When she wears it I think of her as the character in *One Hundred Years of Solitude* who is too good for this earth and floats upwards to heaven.

She doesn't answer. I walk.

I walk towards the shop, the smell of pastries at midnight and no Florence; the street is clear, no junkies, everything dying and fetid beyond the strawberry punnets outside the shop front. A waft of cinnamon, then cigarette smoke, then damp, and I head the wrong way as I figure she wouldn't have turned the right way. Streetlights yawn. Everything is filmed in mould, the light is over-due and under-illuminated under the smog and pus and gangrene of London's spatial uninhabitability.

In one dream she returns. In the other she always returns, and in another, she was never there at all.

Three *Spoonful*

You don't have to be in a strange place to wake up in a strange place. Sometimes you wake before you wake up and the rest of the waking day is a dream working backwards into another terrible deep unconscious blight of the soul. I didn't sleep easy before her. I had sleep paralysis, my sister waking me on the hostel floor because I told her to lift my arm. Never a peaceful night; but then a purring heartbeat next to my shattering sense of safety. I sleep next to the side of the bed nearest the door. She didn't ask me to and I didn't think about it, but I want to be the thing in between her and another nightmare.

And days begin like this: "you gonna score?" "How much should we get? We got £60 last night. We should try and have less. Should we get £60 today?" "Do you think we could be ok on £45?" "£45. Yeah." "What about £90 tonight then we can have plenty then we can just have £45 tomorrow. Do you think that sounds ok?" "Yeah, you have the blood test in ten days so it'll be out by then, if we have £90 now and then we have £45 and we take it easy and then we'll stop on Thursday." "What day is it?"

*

I've got a dealer in mind but he won't answer. I pace and she sits chewing her nails and tries to look angelic. But her face has stretched into an artful panic – if you painted it it'd be a contemporary expression of desperation. "It'll be ok, baby," she says. Her voice cracks a little.

The second guy doesn't answer either. I try to count up the tubes we've left to smoke. Two, maybe there's a third somewhere she's misplaced and forgotten about. And there was that bag we lost under the bed that we never found. She has a few codeine but had all the methadone. We could call Cee and ask for a few tramadol for her; I'd explain she's withdrawing. I run through the options and all of them are like going to find the sea and walking into a cesspit and having to try in vain to make it ok.

Last option: The Trogs. I don't want to go back to them. They're a couple of brothers, thick as pigshit, who would kneecap anyone for twenty pounds. They asked me if I'd do their garden. I hate gardens since I woke up in my mother's in heavy methadone and heroin withdrawal surrounded by dead birds filled with maggots. They pick up. "You around?"

Jewish mother in the street and it's the afternoon, light maniacally fusing my skin with my brain. He walks towards and I see the mother and turn and walk slowly for him to catch up and he starts to shout my name. He shouts louder and louder and I turn around. I turn back and walk slowly, motion for him to follow. He waits next to her by a fucking car. I swallow, chew my mouth and I grit my teeth so hard my eyes sting. I walk towards him and politely try to tell him that drug dealers are supposed to be inconspicuous. He never went to school. He says something unintelligible and I cease to exist in my own cold sweat.

She used to bang up but we're not doing it. She says she can show me, but I say no and she says I'm in charge, which stings a little like it stings when someone says you're kind or generous and you recently said something questionable behind their back after seven cans of super strength. She soothes me, says she's got food but we can't eat it right now because we'll vomit. She says we have to try and eat it later and we agree and somehow all things seem possible, improbable and unnecessary at the same time as I tap the contents of the liquorice-paper wrapped bag onto the foil she prepared two minutes after I left to score.

*

We play Howlin' Wolf's Spoonful through the speakers she paid for with her literary award; the smack we bought with her literary award is strong and she starts gouching half an hour in and making those wounded animal noises she makes when she's high or sick. I lay her out on the bed but she keeps sitting up, lighting a cigarette, then I watch it move close towards the bed in her feeble right hand and place it back in her mouth or in the ashtray and she murmurs, "I'm ok, I'm ok" but the way we're caning it I know I won't be ok and she won't be ok and there's no light in the room and the foil rattles while our housemates move around like skunks beneath us. Rats – the room is a dim dot of blood and we are the light glinting in it. Cells move around and neurons try to communicate but the answer is a slow, heavy roar of ambivalence. And then she's putting a cigarette back in my mouth and growling, "smoke, baby." I pick up the foil and put it down, and then I look for the little coin purse we keep the bags in and there's two missing. I search around on the Indian rug on the bed but can't see because the bags are the same colours as the rug and it takes her several minutes to ask me what I'm doing. I tell her there's two bags missing. "I smoked them," she says. "Is that bad?"

A light flashes on the laptop above the screen and we can see an image of ourselves in a box in the corner. The image of us looks nothing like we feel. She is gouching, her head lolling into her lap. She lifts her head and looks at the image and laughs. "That is us," she says. It's us. The webcam is filming us. I don't know why or who is watching. I run around and find paper and tape and cover it up. My veins twitch and I realise our hovel in space-time is rapidly decreasing to part of the same milieu of rabid rats that live underneath the house. I think of my ex-landlord getting me to watch him smash a rat he found in the living room against the maroon carpet. I think of the Chinese restaurant I used to live above, where I used to sit on the roof with my legs dangling and tell people entering not to go in because of the rat infestation. She picks up the foil. I pick up the foil. She chases and kisses me, blowing the smoke into my mouth. She pulls back and tells me, "we're tripping, you know." Her eyes are gone to the world of nothing left. I shine the lamp light into her face and her pupils are so receded I imagine she can't see me anymore. I tell her it's bad smack. Her headache jumps out of the wardrobe and a door slams. Rain comes through the skylight onto our bed and we watch it fall. Her legs glisten with it, and black marks streak her thighs where the burn on the foil has scummed her hands and I get the baby wipes and erase it. She straddles my lap and begins to kiss me but no matter what we do we can't come when we're stoned. The sex lasts for hours and is the texture of a strawberry and as plump; her mind is gone inside her instincts and she breathes for me then I breathe for her, then I fear one of us ceasing to breathe. The landlady calls up: she needs to feed the depressed snake she keeps in a small tank by our bed and Florence grabs the Indian rug over her naked breasts and we turn our gaze to the dark coil just visible through smoke and the dust in the room and the filthy glass. "I don't know much about snakes but I know when I see a dead thing," she growls. All I can smell is her pussy and all I can taste is the after-tang of smack that needs washing away because it's too real. I shout down to the landlady we're busy and look at the far-darkened, lifeless snake. I rattle on the glass and it stays.

Heroin addicts need sweet things. We drink Ribena as it was her treat at her grandfather's as a child. We eat Jaffa cakes at two in the morning when we're done chasing. She begins to shake as the drug peaks in our system and she says there is a man standing in the dark in our room. She says he wants to hand her a drink of something and what should she do? She closes her eyes and makes the sound of a child crying but without tears.

Four *That Lonesome Valley*

I have to send her away. I always knew I would have to so she wouldn't see me withdraw. It's not something she needs to see. She begged to stay but I remembered days lying in the back seat of a car, other days in a kitchen full of maggots, other days pretending I had the worst possible influenza at my mother's, who never asked me a thing, even when there was nothing left of me but a damp, expressionless face.

I help her pack her things but she over-packs and is sick so I remove some of the unnecessary items – a toy stuffed fox with trippy eyes, more books than she will attempt to read, headscarves she won't wear, a cocktail gown she has no use for. The backpack is made up and I feel like a parent sending their daughter to boarding school. Guilt and fear come into it after the clock turns ten am and I realise her train gets in at twelve at Liverpool Street and we have to leave, I pack her five bags in a small purse she used to keep her headphones in, and her tubes in a plastic baggy, and her clipper lighters, all pink, and her tobacco and Rizlas and filter tips. We're out of foil and I've removed all paraphernalia for my kick. I explain several times that she can't use it all in one go, just one bag a day and one extra, and her tubes for when she runs out, and if she has to come back then she has to, but I need at least two days, although three is better. "Your eyes look haunted," she whispers, holding onto my face.

At the station I can't look at her and she tries to get my attention until the train comes. She wrings her hands and she sighs, cups her face in her hands, sings That Lonesome Valley:

You got to walk that lonesome valley
and you got to walk it by yourself.
Nobody else can walk it for you.
You got to walk that valley for yourself.

When she's gone I think for several seconds that it would be easy to score. She gave me money for food and I walk to the shop like an android and buy two gallon-bottles of water, noodles on offer, cheap biscuits I won't eat, paracetamol and ibuprofen, muscle soak and two tubes of Deep Heat. Then I take it back and walk to Cee's for sleeping pills and amitriptyline. There's chaos in her flat; the woman who lives with her because she blackmails Cee is screaming at a seven-year-old who just stole a chocolate bar from the corner shop. Cee is in the kitchen jacking up and I start to feel the sweat ooze out of the pores on my back. I leave without saying anything, hurting; I text Florence hours in with no reply. Later, I call the friend I sent her to and he says, "she sat on my couch, smoked some heroin, complained about the quality of our tinfoil then fell asleep in her tweed jacket looking like the evil twin of Brian Jones."

*

No one else can go there for you
You got to walk that valley by yourself.

At 4.58am I meld with every moment of lost time from thirty-five years of loss. I notice three texts, and don't read any; her name; she's lost. My legs writhe then my right arm appears to be some-one else's. I move it in front of my face and see it in double, making movements entirely without my permission or volition. The edges of my fingers look purple and my heart palpitates then

I realise it's black from heroin. I haven't washed. I can taste heroin; I fear I got up and scored and used without knowing it sometime in the fug of early morning or sunrise and check my phone. I haven't called anyone. There is virtually no smack in my system. In three days there'll be none. We use the word "clean" to describe having no smack in our systems. I sometimes wonder about the connotations of the antonym for clean – dirty. I look at my black fingers again and my heart beats in stomach acid.

She's lost. She's in Essex somewhere; I wouldn't know how to find her. I can't call her because the sound of her voice would trouble the self-erasing cells inside my flesh and I might vomit them out again. The walls look green and yellow with the skylight blind drawn; enough light to make out the ceaseless silhouette of my own bones but not enough light to be a real person lying here. I sense my double doppelgänger made entirely of anti-matter is lying close and if I just reach out to it I'll be finally annihilated. The amitriptyline knocked me asleep for some hours. However many it needed to get me over the initial terror; I took way too much and I know I could piss or shit myself but can't move. Then I haul myself over the side of the bed and come crashing onto the floor on a black-stained newspaper. I use the sick bowl we always have handy for moments of excessive chasing. When you vomit suddenly on smack it doesn't feel so bad as long as you get to the bowl in time; in fact, it doesn't hurt or feel that disgusting, it's just a thing that happens and when it happens you can resume the caning of heroin. I vomit now like a starved big cat, poisoned by poachers, on the brink of dying in a miserable melee of pain and exhaustion, previously unknown and the last known sensation will be disgust. If they could walk over and kill me outright I'd be grateful. I've been poisoned. I wonder if my pancreas is leaking into my bloodstream or if my heart has become heroin-burn black or just a hole, the light sucking into it from the outside where death is a mirage and we can't see it any more than we can ever really see ourselves. Across the room she is crawling towards the door, and a bird hits the window pane at the south side of the house and my whole physiognomy jumps.

She left me with a blue plastic bag full of prescription drugs to abet my distress. I riffle through it and forget which blister pack is for which and I can't see because of the light and because I'm too weak to retrieve my contact lenses and can't bear to think of wearing them or seeing anything. There's two valium left as we overdo it every time we get them. There's some stomach pills for anti-cramping, there's the Deep Heat, pain relief; I eat two of every pill, chew them until the taste is so repugnant I grab a pint glass of old Ribena by the bed and slug it. It tastes like dust. Something is swimming in the purplish murk. A fly, or...

I lie and try to map all the places in the attic room I may have once hidden heroin or tubes. I talk myself out of looking for them then talk myself back in for three minutes and think it's been hours until I look at the clock on my phone. My hand moves of its own accord before my face, as though it wants to grip my face and suffocate me. I have lost control over it, it's not my hand anymore and it leers and waits.

*

My mother's house, five years ago. I'm lying in the back garden after drinking myself to sleep and when I wake I have no idea where I am or how I got there, wearing nothing but my pants, surrounded by dead birds. Grey birds, brown birds, all dead, some maggot-infested. I'm cold and I can taste vomit but can't move. I look up and the window cleaner is standing over me with a telescopic pole dripping with dirty water from the sponge on top. His horrified expression tells me I am alive.

Maggots in the kitchen I haven't cleaned for weeks. My mother home in two hours and my legs giving way, clawing my way around the kitchen worktops, hand in maggots, a screaming body walking towards louder screams. I look back through the glass door at the dead birds and my childhood cat struts across the lawn, sniffing them in turn, poking them with her paw. I meet her gaze and have to look away in shame. My internal organs feel shrunk and dried out and my stomach has receded so far into my body I think I might shit it out if I cough again.

You conveniently forget the worst withdrawals until the day you're in it deep again. You can even laugh about it, the ridiculous demise and the breakthrough day where you'd rather die than breathe but know you'll be through it in another twenty-four hours, but that's the worst time. Nearing the end of the addiction, this time, you know you want to go back even more, and have no reason to. The pain is alleviated to a manageable level, you have to talk to yourself for fourteen hours of every day and most of it is self-reproach. You only have to call a number. You are angry at the dealers for making it so easy and convenient to score, and angry at the world for not supplying you enough and angry that you live so inhumanely because there is never enough to keep you going indefinitely.

Now the pain has mutated into another kind of pain, a pain only heroin addicts know – like every bone and joint in your body wants to kill you through purest agony. The core of you has collapsed and left scalds and burns and your bones soak up the pain of that, cold to the touch and burnt inside, eyes like two cigarette burns oozing pus.

I write her a letter in my head and cry when I try to explain to her how desperately I need her and how badly I couldn't let her see me like this, but the letter ends with me telling her not to come home, and I heave.

It takes me three hours to get dressed, acclimatise myself to standing up, smoke several cigarettes in succession though they make me retch. The chemist shuts in three more hours and I have to get the train, get there to get my Subutex script; it won't ease it that much but I have to get it back into my system. I am a clinical, medical drug addict, not just a street drug addict. They've kept me supplied for years; I can afford the slips and two and three-day cycles of using because they keep me topped up for free the rest of the time, but Subutex blocks the smack, which puts you into withdrawal, so it takes good management skills to keep both addictions going. I hadn't predicted love would make both so hard – being in it together means we're both smackheads. I had it under control. They never tested me positive for smack, in fact, rarely tested me. I was the quiet, bookish one who didn't make trouble and had no criminal record. They would be happy to keep me on the script for life as long as I don't make trouble. They wouldn't be that concerned about a couple of days off the wagon every now and then, they'd just test me less if they knew.

I can't tie my laces or bend down, but I manage to tuck them in and get through the rickety wooden door to the attic and hold onto the stair rail. My back is wet through already, beads of hot, stinking sweat roll down my sides and my face. I listen for noise downstairs that means the landlady's in. No sound. Then a hacking cough. I have to get through the door without her seeing me but before I've reached the third step she swings open the door and barks in her rough, Germanic voice, "have you got some blue Rizlas? I'm out. And I need some cheese crisps. You're going to the shop, aren't you? You get them for me."

"I'll get you some," I say, but not loudly enough. She barks a noise to indicate I'm not speaking loudly enough. She's half-deaf and fucked on cocaine.

"You want to have dinner with me tonight?" she bleats.

"I have flu," I croak. "I have to go out now."

"Can you get me the cheese crisps, and the blue Rizlas? I'm so poor. I got the cocaine cheap but then I couldn't find my money at home. I think I lost my money."

I try to take my hands away from the bannister to get to the front door but falter and lose balance. She doesn't notice, she notices barely anything. She can't hear herself and she doesn't see anyone. I think she sees birds or lambs, not other people; everyone looking the same, making sounds with their mouths – completely self-orientated and dumb. She is a gaping mouth that only ever opens in want. "Which cheese crisps?"

"I don't know what they're called. They're cheesy."

"That narrows it down."

"In a yellow packet. Those ones. And I can't smoke green Rizlas, so get the blue ones, yes? Oh, and milk. And if you have a spare fiver, I'll have that too. I need things. I really am so poor." She sniffs.

She thinks we're in a relationship and invites herself up to my room. She refers to Florence as "your friend" as in, "is your *friend* still staying with us?" I feel like shouting, "yes, in my bed, don't you hear us fucking our brains out?" but I say nothing as the tenancy is not especially secure.

Outside, the street pulses with a radiating, toxic light and I wonder how anyone can go out in it. I cover my eyes with my hand and stagger towards the main road to get to the train station while the gypsy pickpocket three doors up cycles around me in circles, grinning. A car pulls up; red, small, the window rolls down and a black guy nods at me from the driver seat, and I have no idea why I'm doing it even as I'm doing it but I climb automatically into the passenger seat and he smiles a forced cracked-tooth smile and my eyes are drawn to the bag in his lap. I've never seen the guy before. He has oversized ears and teeth but is otherwise handsome.

He says some patois shit to me and offers me a discount on three bags. I tell him no but he puts one bag in my hand and leans in, says, "sample. Tell your friends. I got the best gear." I take his number in my phone and he says, "one love, fam," as I climb out of the car, wincing.

At the end of the road I go to turn with the "sample" in my inner breast pocket; I can be at the station in five minutes' time. A black car pulls up next to me, a saloon, I see the flash of movement then the window rolls down automatically; a white guy, bald, practically toothless. A European accent: "get in."

His T's are over pronounced and rattle against my teeth. He checks his mirrors then reaches across me into the glove compartment, takes out a small, black bag and reels off a list of substances, sniffing intermittently. He gives me discount deals if I take some today. He says, "weed your thing? Got Moroccan and shit. The shit. You can take some, show your friends. I've got the best gear. Tell everyone." I think about telling him I don't use, but realise it'd sound ridiculous as I'm drenched and shaking. He looks me over and takes out three bags of smack, wrapped in blue plastic.

*

I can't stand up on the train and an old man tells me to take his seat. I take it and he gives me a painful look of sympathy. Even my jeans are wet. My hair is wet. I shiver against the window, looking out at the embankments, thinking of the fox litter that lived in my garden in the flat next to the train line, shuddering every few minutes when a train rattled past and running for cover. Vigilant? I wasn't vigilant enough; never had two dealers in one day accost me on my own street. I have a pocketful of smack and it'd see me through the next 48 hours if I spaced it out. And then what?

I can feel it next to my heartbeat. I can taste the way it would taste and I think of the preparation, the foil, the relief; a sunburst halo of relief; a warmed gut and a headless body, not trammelled into nothing more than a pang of regret and need. But I would care that I let her down. She would not. She would tell me it's ok and use again. The bottle of methadone I procured for her return cost me. I wrapped it in two paper bags and two carrier bags and hid it in the safe. It's a green dot on my map of putting things right; it's the central entity; two more days and she'll start on it and I'll be clean. I alight at Dalston and walk the block, past the market, looking out for dealers so I can avoid more encounters. London is the shame of a black eye I don't want to look at anymore. There's a stench of fish and Halal meat. People buy weed from the butcher on the market. Chickens are strung up. Fistfuls of stolen fruit in hands walk up and down and across me. There's a waft of perfume and skunk. Two girls kiss one man in an alleyway. An overweight woman looking bored and exhausted solicits by the back street to my left. An unavoidable lunatic behind me whispers something about the book of Genesis. The flat to my right, above my head, they're doing a stakeout and the dealers neglect to care. A fever makes my eyes sting and I wish I could run. Heroin burns holes all over.

The pharmacist tries to fuck with me and says he doesn't have my script, smiling. He does it nearly every time so I just sit down. He asks me how I've been. I tell him I'm getting married next week. He asks where I'm getting married and I tell him Honduras.

When I get back to our street I call her. She sounds delighted, breathy and stoned, and relays her usage and how well she's doing. "I don't use during the day or even first thing in the morning! I get to five pm and then I chase and I've started feeling rough by then, but if I leave it til six tomorrow, then I'll be home with you the next day, and I've spaced it out so I won't run out."

"Still got your tubes?"

"Yeah, I've kept them."

"You'll get more stoned off them, remember. They'll see you through."

"I miss you so much, baby. How you doing?"

I breathe, rattling.

"Are you coping?"

I tell her about the two dealers who drove up on our street as I was going to the pharmacy.

"Did you score?"

"I got samples. I'm giving them away, I don't want them. I'll give them to Cee. I just can't believe it, I'm withdrawing to fuck and they give me drugs. Do I have 'smackhead' written on my forehead or something? Do I look like a smackhead?"

"No, baby, you look loved," she purrs. I cry and tell her I have to go and she'll be ok. She starts talking, she says, "it's like when Jesus was approached by the devil before his crucifixion, baby. You're doing so well."

I have to go and I hang up. The phone is a foreign object in my hand. I can't hear her voice, it's almost not her voice. I hear the way she'll plead with me for heroin; I hear the need in her voice, the way she's convinced she's kicking. I hear the heroin in her voice. It drags me into bed and I berate myself in a whirlpool of self-denigration as my legs kick under the sheets that still smell of her.

Five *Something Inside of Me*

That white rabbit I took in to save it from the small box Andreas kept him in was pink-eyed; I feared him, his sideways gaze. Nothing in front of him, only vigilance and twitching. I let him jump around my room at night though he often didn't move much, his sudden movements across the room made me jerk. He infiltrated my nightmares and I forget his name, even now. I cared for many things before heroin.

Being kicked out of the flat in Bethnal Green, I realised London was exploding in the future and the explosion resonated back into the past like it was always going to do as none of us were going anywhere. I was offered a flat in Merseyside by a man in an office who said they wanted "us" out. I was earning and the flat was ideal; snotty neighbours aside, I made it there on my own; a canal, a good bed, a clean floor. The EastEnders actress being murdered and cut up and dumped in a suitcase in the canal next to the flat blighted it only a little. You accepted there was death everywhere you looked if you really did live in London, not just the idea of it.

I called home to try and get help with a deposit on a room. The mum was drunk and stoned on "jazz cabbage" and I could hear a dog barking that wasn't theirs; another "friend" of my mother's had come over to sell her weed. Lung cancer didn't stop her; it just deadened our feelings of hope that she would ever retrieve herself. The house smelled of shit and I wasn't even in it. I could tell just by listening to her wail on the phone. Everything was shit again. I told her I was being made homeless and she reminded me about the compensation claims I could've made after the accident. Poor people shouldn't be given £60,000 when they won't use it on anything other than pain relief.

The mum had told me things no son or daughter should ever hear. I wanted her to stop but she shrieked uncontrollably and swore. I thought about all the friends she'd sent me to, sent me away with, waking up with them in my bed, or that time she took me out with one of them picking mushrooms in some fields and I cut my arm open on barbed wire and the "friend" who was obviously fucking her had to carry me in his arms and rush me to hospital. That was as close to love as I'd known by any male figure. She was tripping by nightfall that evening. The arrow-shaped scar on my arm that points to my veins still reminds me of her.

I wanted to love something and didn't know how to find that thing. If it were to be a woman I didn't find her and couldn't see how she would find me. Drizzle in the hostel, twenty-four-hour noise, parties in the adjacent rooms a third of the size of the attic we live in, if not less than a third, and some kind of bumping, thudding looped noise I can't consider music. Ex-cons laid in bed in their own stink, naked with the doors open. Withdrawing junkies shitting themselves. Men who are trans and have never told a soul wore dresses in their box rooms and kept themselves to themselves. There were cockroaches from the beginning of time. The noise of the market, the ruckus of soliciting, the calling out and calling out to spend money to keep the traders in their own single box rooms living off anything other than the food they sell. Drunks, dealers, car crashes, picket lines outside the cinema, racial abuse, misogynistic whistles, reggae and the stink of dead flesh and rancid food from the back alleys and restaurants where the rats have their Saturday night kebab parties and copulate in the dustbins. Constant, unbearable heat from the fixed radiators that you couldn't turn down or turn off. Wishing I was in Alaska in isolation as a way of getting to sleep for thirty minutes at a time and no more. Waking paralysed, some idiot banging on my door, raving about some other idiot banging on his wall raving about some other idiot bashing someone's head in.

When I moved into the attic room through a friend whose

wife had sent him to Portugal because of his rampant alcoholism, I lived by stealing Magnum ice cream lollies from the communal freezer in the mouse-infested kitchen. The ice creams were for the obese woman who couldn't walk who lived in the downstairs front room and who no one ever saw or spoke about. She had MS and an online shopping addiction. The whole of the downstairs stunk of her piss and no one seemed to want to mention it. She was a sweet woman who assumed from our first meeting I was gay.

I get so close to erasing myself I have to write something down and stare at it to know my thoughts are real, and really mine, and my head is real, and my consciousness is a perceptible thing. Since I moved here the landlady has become more and more deluded about our relationship and her cocaine addiction neither helps me, nor her, nor the financial situation of the house overall, but then cocaine is only useful for stretching reality to breaking point on a minute-to-minute basis. Bentley lives in the room below me with his girlfriend who most people call Mogadon, though she's kind and self-conscious and I feel for her. Bentley was in a cult in America and had to be rescued but he hasn't shaken the indoctrination and looks like a Belsen camp victim now. Sometimes I have an urge so visceral to hit him in the face when he waffles on to me about poverty as though it excludes myself and himself, and I have to swallow and return to the attic and play Robert Johnson and chase smack to calm down. And the landlady's attempts to sleep with me are increasingly pernicious. Florence says she probably used to masturbate in my bed when I wasn't there, and in front of Florence she once drunkenly exclaimed that she needed sex badly, "filthy fucking sex." I told her to shut up, but Florence was laughing about it as it was so ridiculous, and had force fed her fried chicken so she could drive us back from the gig she drove us to, when she turned to Florence and exclaimed, "you're going to have your tit cut off, no one will want you then!"

Florence didn't bat an eyelid as venom doesn't affect her. Later, she put my hand on her breast and asked me if I would still want her as it was likely her breast would be removed in the coming months. I think she already knows what I think and feel, often before I do. I didn't have to say anything; she pressed her naked breasts into my ribcage and we slept like that.

I move my arm over her side of the bed where she is absent. She returns tomorrow still loaded with smack and it begins for her. I won't tell her anything. I won't prepare her as the methadone will ease it, and maybe she'll be ok. I don't want her to hurt like I am hurting; the thought of it unhinges my stomach from its pit in my inexcusably burdened body. My muscles now feel both flaccid and tense, there is no end to the pain because no matter how far in you are when you kick, time begins to sprawl so you can only crawl toward the home strait.

Her pink nightgown hangs on a hanger on the wardrobe door, empty, billowing slightly in the breeze from the open skylight. I need to get the stench of heroin withdrawal out of the room before she arrives. Sweat-stained sheets, ash, the cloying smell of a body pushed through its limits, adrenaline, puke. The light filtering in shows the dust floating around in the fetid air; and then she's there in the nightgown, her insides turning rotten with inhaling all this. There's no warmth where she doesn't sleep. She's wondering why I don't respond to her and it's because it hurts me to feel the true depth of my adoration – you have so much to lose, I tell myself. If it's lost this is all there is – the room, an old lady trying to fuck you, a pit, a shell, more things pawned, borrowed and mislaid in time. Absolutely no music can take away the sound of the unredeemable state of panic you live in in withdrawal. It's better to hear nothing at all, and when it goes dark I turn the light out early so I don't have to glimpse myself in any reflective surfaces, because if this is what she sees when she looks at me, I wish she were blind or I was not this chronic smackhead with a corroding nervous system.

I find the notebook she keeps for me when I go out for any length of time, with messages to help me. It's a sweet and funny thing, not to be taken seriously. One page reads, "DO NOT GO TO THE PEMBURY TAVERN UNDER ANY CIRCUMSTANCES. YOU WILL FIND YOURSELF LISTENING TO ASSHOLES TALKING ABOUT THEIR OWN SHIT ALL NIGHT AND JUST WISH YOU WERE WITH ME."

Who is She?

That question was only relevant for the first hour after meeting her in the late-night bar which was crawling with hipsters and 70s throwbacks at two am and I'd only gone to get the twenty pounds Dwayne owed me for cheap tobacco I picked up from the guy outside Seven Sisters station. I'd agreed to one pint because the boredom and fear of the landlady walking in high on coke was too much to bear. It was a Wednesday night, I'd scored in the morning and had used most of the gear and I needed the money back as a matter of urgency.

I didn't see her enter the bar; I saw Dwayne turn his head as she walked over to us and I know she recollects none of what happened in there. She didn't appear to realise I was an actual human being at the time, and propped herself up on my shoulder telling Dwayne she'd drunk four bottles of wine and had four grams of coke and didn't want to go to bed. Dwayne spoke slowly and smiled and I could see that even after four bottles of wine the cogs in her head turned about seven times faster than his. I thought she was hitting on him, I guess. It had started to arouse annoyance in me that she hadn't bothered to speak to me, look at me or engage with me. I thought she was mad. She wore a cream suede coat with a cream fur trim and had tight jeans on with a lumberjack-type check shirt and trainers. Dwayne remarked that he'd never seen her dressed like that, when she went to the bathroom and came back sniffing and wiping her nose. I didn't ask what she usually wore but with her flicked eyeliner and smoky, lilac-shimmered eyes I assumed she usually overdressed. The bartender called for last orders and I think she downed a double vodka spritzer to "put her on" and we walked her outside and I rolled two cigarettes and gave her one. She then appeared to notice me for the first time and let go of Dwayne and looked at me for a while, and I said, "you're from Manchester, aren't you?" for no apparent reason. She said she was and seemed amazed as her accent was not Mancunian. I realised Dwayne was itching to take her home and I felt sorry for her. I had a powerful sense that I couldn't let her be another notch on an idiot's bedpost. I also noticed she was highly attractive stood under the streetlamp, and her hair was a mess, and I could feel the sadness of closing time was a palpable thing for her. I got the distinct impression this day and night were the way every day and night went for her; she was so obviously a habitual drug user and anyone who is in the same bar at closing time in London every night has a drink problem. She asked me which way I was walking, and I pointed in the direction she was also walking. She asked me if I could walk her home and Dwayne said, "I'm going the other way, anyway," and trundled off with a sulky expression and a yawn. Then sobriety seemed to overcome her as instantly as she saw my face and we began to walk towards Stamford Hill, turning into her street, smoking a second cigarette. She said, "I have shitloads of cocaine in my purse if you want some. Can we hang out for a bit?" I said, "yeah, I suppose you can come to mine for a bit but I want to go to sleep in an hour and will have to kick you out." She nodded in assent, like a seven-year-old who had been bribed with a chocolate bar if they did maths homework; then she left me at the porch of her block of flats and told me to wait for her.

When she reappeared, she handed me a book. A book she'd written and had been published. I almost couldn't look at it and said I'd read it over the weekend as I was going to visit my sister in Manchester. In forty-eight hours I'd be up there. I needed sleep and smack; all the way back I tried to figure out how to tell her I'd need to use and pretend I wasn't an addict, but the conversation quickly became about drugs and she told me she was a cocaine addict. I asked her about heroin, tentatively, as we watched car headlights blink by and smoke rise, and smog coagulate and fade and drunken yells peak, and she said, "it's my favourite drug." I asked her if she'd used this last year while she'd lived in London, and she said she had avoided it but she had developed a "slight problem" with morphine. She said her coke dealer wouldn't sell her smack. "I guess he makes more money out of selling me the coke," she added. "It's fucking expensive."

She told me about the literary awards where she was bullied by some older, white playwright who wouldn't relent and told her, "you don't deserve to be seated next to me," and "you must have slept with all the judges to get on this prize list." She told me how she had to score coke to deal with that kind of thing, how it made her want to lock herself away, how the entirety of her life had been lonely, how much she wanted to not be alone anymore. I realised she was not mad, and was relieved, and worried, and the hours flew by and I couldn't let her go.

We bought a can each from the all-night shop and I told her to hold her breath when we entered the house because of the piss smell and she dutifully held her breath and climbed sweetly to the attic. I had to keep telling her to be really quiet; she asked if I was allowed people around and I told her I don't give a fuck but don't like anyone knowing my business. We sat at my desk and she racked up several lines and it turned out she did in fact have another four grams or so of coke and was definitely up for using it all. "I want rid of it," she said. "I don't want to be doing it anymore. Let's just get rid of it tonight. It's really got to stop."

"Do you think you'll score some more tomorrow?" I asked.

"Of course I fucking will."

*

Night ebbed like a period of fasting into dawn, and then I sensed she'd leave when she asked for coffee. We were blinded by four grams of cocaine and every book we'd ever loved dissected over a Black and Decker table with a filled ashtray. Her feet were tucked under her where she sat at my office chair, socked-feet, an expression of trust and fear of morning. I had to chase, and I made out like I'd just found some left over on some foil in my room and offered her some, but she said, "no, it's yours." By nine am she was going to leave to go back to her box room, bathe and then come back and I'd score heroin. The comedown preceded the actual comedown and we both sat gazing into past worlds held together with nothing more than anticipation and dread of being alone again.

Leaving together, avoiding my landlady somehow, we walked to a shop to buy food and though she wasn't hungry she insisted I eat something so I wouldn't feel worse when she returned. I couldn't eat so I bought a nutrition drink, something I was prone to relying on, and we discussed the best flavour, but I chose her least favourite. She said chocolate milkshake had saved her life and told me how she stole a bottle of Slim Fast every day from the local supermarket, to "put her on."

Morning light was a painful accumulation of several years of delayed headache. The sun was high and unmerciful, and we strode towards Stamford Hill where she took out a large sum from the ATM and handed it to me. We arranged to meet back there in a few hours, when I'd been to the chemist in Dalston, and she'd bathed, and I wondered why she was giving a stranger so much money and wanted to assure her I wouldn't steal it without letting on it occurred to me I could steal it, and never would have, if only to see her again. And she walked.

I watched her walk towards the meeting point near the station. She wore a black skirt with red flowers, a white short-sleeved blouse, her hair untidier than it had been, full make-up with red lips, bleary, squinting in the sun, her skirt swaying with her hips as she moved seamlessly towards me. I told her I'd already had some; I was sorry; I had to. I told her she must be feeling like shit and I felt for her because I'd had a pain from my nose through my eye sockets and into my head for hours. I said it'll soon be better. I could tell she didn't want me to look at her, and got her through the front door and up the stairs and back into the room she'd left emptier.

She asked if she could lie down on my bed and laid herself out with her feet at the pillows, barefoot, little flame-red nails, dark hair splayed like a gunshot wound above her skull. She had breasts like Molly Bloom's. Her legs were milk white and sculpted, the skirt riding further up, moans and laughter. Her hand palm upturned over the side of the bed, she asked me if she could touch mine. I asked why.

She asked if I could lay down with her, but I avoided it. We'd spent less than twenty-four hours together and all of it high. And we could. But would she go further away, and if she didn't come back what would I be left with, now I'd been so close to her? The day became a sunbeam in a vault in a dark, odourless, soundless chamber.

Sometimes a person remembers the first time they experienced overwhelming pain as an event, and sometimes, a person recalls the relief from overwhelming pain as an event in their life; the receding of pain; and this becomes the central fixation throughout their lives – how to achieve the cessation of pain, in the full understanding of how unbearable it is to suffer.

We could not let go of our first experiences of opiates. She remembers hearing the sound of her own slow breath at full volume, reverberating around a hospital room, and previously, the first stint as a heroin addict and how unbearable it was to feel anything beyond the needle.

There is nothing more wonderful in this world than morphine. Street heroin can only come so close to the purity of intravenous morphine, and any amount of pain seems a feasible price to pay to live within the ever-loving, maternal arms of high-grade opiate drugs. The risks are there but they shut themselves away in bedrooms, attending to whatever they attend to, and don't show themselves, and because they are not seen often, they need not be taken into consideration. On smack you slim down to a very pure entity. All the regrets, troubles and memories that were fixed onto you or gnawing at your insides popped out of your body and went very far away.

The risks for her as a cocaine addict were immeasurable, waiting down dark streets in the early hours of the morning when the drug had run out and was threatening to hand her brain over to incomprehensible melancholy. She spoke of dealers who would lock the doors and drive her further than she asked to go, how she'd have to put up a fight to get out of the car, how one of them leaned in and bit her mouth until it bled, how they tried to solicit her for "parties." One regular dealer had told her he wanted to take her to a five-star hotel room, rub cocaine into her pussy and "bang her" with his dick. He told her he loved Dostoyevsky and MILFS.

She had about a thousand reasons to use drugs. I had about a thousand more. But I saw myself as a drug addict, a smackhead, and I saw her as something else, though she didn't. I wondered how she could see me through the grime of drug addiction; I'd stopped looking after myself, had lost so much weight, had started going weeks without ever looking in a mirror, cutting my hair with broken paper scissors. Someone who once knew me had seen me in the street and described me as looking like "a dead homeless ghost." Then she came back from a trip to see her kid, broken, and we met up at the station where we always met and her step quickened as she recognised me there, and we hugged, as we always hugged, and walked to mine to use drugs, talk, watch movies, have indoor picnics, talk, not touching.

She couldn't have loved me, I was sure of it.

We met in Tesco one afternoon after I'd stood her up in Brixton. I'd seen a film of her on the BBC, reading poetry into the camera, powdered skin, a white silk blouse, pink lips. There was not even an echo of a smile. I became so mesmerised I missed our "date" and phoned her to apologise and she didn't seem to mind, just came back over to Hackney and said she'd cook for me in her flat. Her flatmate would be out for the evening. We planned a meal: toad-in-the-hole. I was late even to the supermarket and found her in the fruit aisle, where she threw her arms around my shoulders and we laughed. I didn't know what we were doing, I just followed her through the various aisles and she picked out ingredients, paid for them, and we took the bus to her place where she seemed afraid her flatmate might not have gone out after all, though it was peaceful, a balcony door still open, a breeze. In her room she'd bought fragranced candles to get rid of the smell of heroin. There were boxes of foil stuffed in her clothes-cupboard. She began making the food and we started chasing in her room, surrounded by her Dante and Shelley, and I sat on her tiny black metal-framed child's day-bed, more pillows than bed. It was a bed she never got more than a couple of hours' sleep in. She lit candles and listened for the door, and the food burned.

We wanted to live, to have the things other people seemed to have – security, financial stability, love. But we also wanted the life that sheltered us from experience, pain and the effects of time constantly churning and passing and all the longing and regret that comes with that. The moment is cruel, without a buffer or a way of turning the volume down. I could see everything she felt just by looking at her face, and she could see into me in a way that made me avoid her gaze.

Her landlady returned a little after nine pm, flounced into the kitchen where we were sat talking and eating the burnt food which was still highly edible as slightly charred tastes appeal to us. She didn't make eye contact with me, or speak to me directly. She complained about "carbs" and said she wouldn't eat any of the food. She told Florence, "you eat nothing but breakfast cereal these days," in a scoffing tone. I'd never heard anyone speak to a person they lived with such a potent air of disgust at their existence. She shoved me out of the way of the fridge door, threw herself about the room and made it impossible for us to stay. We hid all paraphernalia in the box room, sprayed deodorant to mask the smell of smack, picked up a few books she wanted me to read, and walked into the night. I could see her shoulders relax in the open air – we rolled smokes and pretended to ourselves that it would be better if only we could remain stoned, on our own, together, unaffected by the oppressive gaze of others. She said she could never feel guilty for getting hooked in someone else's flat when it seemed like their every move was designed to bully her into some kind of silence. Florence said she knew she wasn't wanted there but what scared her landlady more was losing her money. It didn't stop her walking in, shouting about there being no milk, making passive-aggressive statements in place of any kind of mutual communication. Florence said being "motherless" made you feel these things worse; she said although it was men who'd done her the most physical harm, it was women who'd caused her the most lasting damage. Living in a box room, paying half the rent on a flat twenty times the size of her room, Florence seemed beaten down by a woman twice her size; she said she knew how to keep men in line but she felt she was being eroded by the presence of this woman who very often sat across from her and watched her eat without lifting her eyes to see the usual mouth-agape expression of vile hatred in her landlady. Taking the shit her landlady couldn't give to all the people who'd walked away sooner than Florence could, I could see how much she physically shrank when this woman returned, slamming all the doors in the flat before walking into her room unannounced to initiate some kind of interrogation or argument. I reminded her homelessness is one of the most exploitable states of being; being homeless and semi-famous was always going to bring out the leeches.

*

A phone call later that week indicated something had devastated her through a soporific haze, and she asked me if she might be able to come stay with me for the night. I picked her up and we walked; almost silently, discussing at times the finer points of British contemporary poetry, or the underbelly of it, which was the world that had invited her to abuse everything she was.

She told me about her living arrangements, how untenable they'd become now that the landlady stormed about like a homicidal whirligig, seemed to want to intrude upon every aspect of her existence. How she shook each morning before she had to walk out of the box room, expecting to be accosted or grilled over something she'd done, said, somewhere she'd been, a comment made about her at a literary event, or just that she hadn't done something right, again. And maybe, Florence had mused one time stoned, maybe she was right about one thing – that she didn't do anything right. But anyone who was upset with someone about doing something wrong could only make a valid argument if they themselves were so clean of wrongdoing or mis-endeavour they "visibly gleamed gloatingly, like a saint without genitals." She told me one night of all the figures watching her, brooding, waiting for her to slip or fall, killing her with imperatives meant to share their own happiness. She said, "I know not one person whose own morality is not obscenely bloated. Only you. There are people who wish me ill and people who want me dead, but I just want to be disappeared where you are." She added, "you would think there were no mirrors in London. None of the assholes in it ever seem to look at themselves." London to her was a thing, a mire or a black lagoon or a suicide forest or a bloated heart infested with scurrying, narcissistic creatures she could not understand. She said living in that flat was like living in a place black with unfeasible anger, never had she been around someone so angry with everyone but herself. I saw it that day, the tiny kids' bedroom still full of the landlady's stuff, like she could take only so much floor and air space and no more. It was like everywhere I'd ever crashed or lived in London.

Everyone in this place is so fucking clean. Until they are witnessed. But of course, most people don't look, and they keep it all hidden under the bed.

We watched the film Drive, stoned, half hoping it would condense into a ten-minute montage without the blood warped chiaroscuro. Time was a mucus-strewn London-binge-drunk night-sky, and nothing more stretched out before us but the point at which we would be separated again. I began to make a bed on the floor to sleep on; she climbed into my bed and asked me why we couldn't both sleep there. It would be warmer, easier, and it was my bed after all; I couldn't sleep on the floor, and she wouldn't let me.

She lay beside me in a dress riding up to her waist and whispered with her warm cigarette-heroin breath, "I feel safe only here."

Eight *Blues Before Sunrise*

A friend's mother, who I'd always considered more of a mother to me than my own, gave us her half-a-million-pound flat in Walthamstow for almost a month to airlift us out of the hell that had become the oppressive, fetid attic we were accustomed to in South Tottenham. We'd have cooking facilities, a lounge, and a bedroom with no one listening in. After visiting my friend to pick up the keys, before his mother left for Florence, Italy, he reported she'd described my Florence as a "Jewish mama." She'd been wearing the charity-shop polka dot, navy blue dress she bought from the Jewish quarter; she never intended to look Jewish but her black-dyed hair and housewife-vintage gave her an air of Jewish housewife. Jewish women would gather in the aisles in supermarkets and watch us, wondering what she was doing with me. The checkout assistant in the kosher supermarket where she liked to buy food would speak to her in Yiddish, and the days when she wore red lipstick and chain-smoked through the streets, members of the community in their black wigs would tut in our direction.

The flat in Walthamstow had a deep-red front door, loud brass knocker, and it could be accessed on the first floor via a dusty staircase. We had not known luxury like it in the time we'd spent together, and after sleeping on various sofas for £150 a week, and in the "UK's worst hostel" according to a TV documentary, I found myself wandering into rooms unsure of where I wanted to be – the choice had either been bed, sofa or floor before. There was a rocking chair with a hippy throw, a large kitchen with an oak dining table and a bed we could feel safe and undisturbed in.

But then there was the heroin; to score I'd have to get on the train back to South Tottenham, and we were fresh into it again – the five-day methadone plan had worked for her after I withdrew in the attic. She was stoned out of her mind on the green juice, and I had to hide it and meter it out to her daily until the sixth day when she began taking tramadol after procuring several boxes from a friend who was also a junkie. The tramadol was a good source of income for our friend; if you were an addict it always made sense to try to get any prescription drugs you could to sell on, whether you needed them or not. You never needed anything more than the smack for yourself. Florence said she was taking a few a day for the pain in her breast with her condition, but I didn't monitor it or feel the need to. Back on smack she didn't take them at all. A couple of nights in I realised we'd have to stop again. It was not something I could easily put to her; and when I did it was less of a question or suggestion than a fact I would insist upon, "we stop on Tuesday," or whatever day seemed like the last possible day we could use without becoming heavily addicted again. When you've been addicted once, no matter how long you were hooked, the hook gets into you far sooner, and it's far harder to extricate from. She knew this and ignored the addiction symptoms, so it was ever down to me to try and rein it in. I'd been addicted for years; the only thing that made me need to stop was her. I'd made her a smackhead again, and didn't like to think of it; and then sat at that oak table or in the big bed she'd suck up on that grey wisp and smile at me like a child after secret candy. She knew what she was doing as much as I did; she just preferred to defer such things as recognising the truth about the damage we could cause ourselves.

*

On heroin there was less reason to cook, eat, or do anything much. We couldn't sleep because it caused severe insomnia. The heroin often made us buzzy, talking for hours, interrupting each other, or just gouching out on the bed or in chairs, separately, conscious of each other's presence and heightened state but too fucked to come back into full lucidity. We didn't want to be lucid, nor did we have to be. And so, the flat filled with crumpled, filthy, blackened tinfoil and dead clipper lighters, Rizla packets, ashtrays, sick-bowls, her lingerie screwed up in piles on the floor. Everything dirty, elegantly so, and pointlessly wonderful.

She'd reach the point where she couldn't really speak anymore, or her speech was a growl or a low purr as opposed to articulated language constructed from understandable utterances. Sometimes we wanted to kiss and touch, but couldn't always put the foil down for long; maybe at four or five am when the gear had run low, we'd get into bed together and hold each other. She'd become overwhelmed with heat and feelings of adoration and climb onto me or into me or over me or under me and whisper and kiss my skin and start to become breathless with thoughts and sensations too incorruptibly all-encompassing to bear. We'd cry, often, in each other's arms, at the beauty and fragility; always one wrong step away from disaster or one step closer to death. Closer to loss; never further from it. Time, for us, was not linear. It never had been, and never would be again.

*

I dreamt I was in a basement in a mental asylum and there was nothing more to me than an arm. I was a single arm fastened to a wall with handcuffs, light coming through the floorboards above, the occasional footfall of nurses or doctors or patients. Shadows, clinking, muffled sounds. A dark room which smelled of rancid feet; no body and nobody.

The clinking, shuffling and groaning above me became more audible and my fist tightened and pulled at the cuff it was fastened to but couldn't free itself. Several men in black suits, wearing velvet-black fedoras entered the basement and stood over me. I was white and wet with sweat.

She shook me awake with her right hand, then grasped herself either side of her arms, across her chest as though she was freezing. "I'm sick, baby. I'm really sick." Jaw clenched, she exited, and I heard her vomiting violently in the bathroom next door. She returned and sat on the bed dripping with piss, shivering and splaying her legs out in front of herself then drawing them back, then curling up on the bed with her legs drawn into her stomach, occasionally vocalising pain or emitting pitiful noises. Light returned to the room within the hour and I lost my contact lenses and couldn't fully focus on her face as she sat in front of me and begged me to score.

I left the room to piss and saw there was piss all over the floor around the toilet and vomit in the sink. She made sounds like a small animal suffering some terminal type of pain; through the wall it sounded more disturbing still. I checked the door was locked and hid the keys, returned to the bedroom where she seemed semi-conscious by the window on the right side of the bed, covers ruffled around her still-kicking legs. I found the boxes of tramadol she'd been using for some time and they were all empty. At least 200 tablets gone in a couple of weeks. I checked her handbag and found nothing but change, Rizlas and chewing gum. I checked for the last of the codeine she'd been prescribed but there were none. I checked the small, black purse we kept our gear in, though the scene in the kitchen suggested she'd finished it earlier in the night and hadn't slept since. A 150-page manuscript had been printed off and left on the oak table in the kitchen. A note on top of it read, "been up all night. I did it!"

When she woke and was able to stand, I walked her to the kitchen, though it seemed the use of her legs was compromised by the pain she was in. She told me several times, "it hurts all over.

What's wrong with me?" I asked her where all the tramadol had gone and she told me she'd had almost all of it. I asked her how many she'd been taking a day and she replied, "I dunno. Ten? Or something like that. I *needed* them."

I told her there was no more gear and she stopped still, looked into my face as her legs ceased to move as they had been doing for hours. She said, "I need some. I have numbers. I took them from your phone and I'm going to use them. I'll go out and I'll use them. I need drugs. I can't feel like this. Either you go and get me some or I'll do it." Her words began to hiss. I told her I couldn't do that, and she'd be ok, it'd be a few days and it wouldn't be as bad as last time.

"It is! It is so much fucking worse, and you need to help me. You're not the only one who suffers this. It's not one rule for you and one for everyone else. I'm dying! Are you just going to watch me? I am not fucking doing this. I will not fucking do this. No I won't. I will not. You fucking go out and you fucking score. I'll get out, I'll jump out the fucking window. I'll ring the police and I'll say you kidnapped me. I'll tell them I don't even know who you are if you don't fucking get me some fucking heroin."

An hour later there were spiders running over her feet which she couldn't catch. She stopped speaking at all later in the evening. I imagined it was hurting me as much as it was hurting her but then I remembered the worst hours of my life in withdrawal and knew that couldn't possibly be true. She died slowly for the next three days as the bed absorbed so much sweat we had to dry out the mattress, then one morning she brought me porridge in bed and told me she was sorry for everything and cried like a child, grief-stricken and so sorry.

Nine *Crossroad*

The first day she left the flat she came back an hour later saying a man with a huge pair of scissors had asked her if she wanted a haircut outside the tube station on Blackhorse Lane. Everywhere we went there seemed to be more people on the streets made crazy by poverty. On one of our many A&E visits, because she was in pain in her breast or needed pain relief, a man had turned to us in the waiting area to tell us he had tried to kick a man to death in a cage fight and his leg was broken. He tried to look each of us in the eye and tell us about it; she made no eye contact whatsoever and I made limited eye contact as he was looking for someone to fight. He was in only ten minutes or so when the doctor called him in and sent him away again, limping.

We'd seen a lot at Homerton hospital, where she saw a consultant regularly. She described arriving there one night for morphine and seeing a man with a carrier bag holding something which was dripping blood onto the floor. She said he'd become quieter and quieter sat in his chair across from her, his head lilting forwards into his lap. A nurse placed an absorbent pad underneath him, the kind you use to toilet-train puppies and after several hours had passed checked to see if he was breathing, and as he was, she left him again. Another hour passed and he was percolating pink and grey foam from his mouth which slowly dripped onto the blue absorbent pad. Eventually he keeled over. It was some time before anyone attended to him.

The day arrived when I had to take her to have surgery to remove the mass in her breast that had been making her ill since I met her. It would be removed, tested, and she'd need a period of recovery. It was unlikely the whole breast would be removed but it was possible. We smoked cigarettes in the cold outside the hospital, psychiatric patients wandered by asking us for cigarettes, telling us we needed to drink boiled water out of a kettle every day to get well. That they were consultants once. That their advice was worth two cigarettes. She recalled giving one of them a whole packet of tobacco one day outside A&E, because she was high, and that particular man remembered her and said she never had to give him any again, and bowed his head as though to royalty.

We found the ward and sat for no more than five minutes before a list of names was shouted from the front of the waiting room. Her name was first, and around fifteen patients gathered in a nervous grouping by the entrance to the surgical ward. I stood with her and was told no relatives would be allowed in. People shifted and looked at the closed doors. Then she was taken, with the group, through the double doors, and when they closed, locking automatically, I sat in the waiting room all day. It was around five or six hours until the first woman staggered back out through the double doors, alone, fell against a wall, staggered again, and no one came to help her. The woman at the reception desk continued to file her nails; the daytime TV continued its advertisements for payday loans and debt consolidation. She eventually found her way to the exit and was gone.

In the next hour, several more solitary figures came through the doors; one collapsed and help had to be called. Many more asked for help, a phone call, a taxi service, and were mainly ignored or told without eye contact to go home and rest.

Then she came through the doors, a little ruffled, looking slightly confused, pale, dreamy and desperate to leave. I walked over to her and she whispered, "let's get the fuck out of here. I woke up and asked what I needed to do to get out and they said, 'pass urine', so I grabbed a jug of orange squash, downed it and squeezed one out." We got outside, smoked, took a cab back to Walthamstow, and she was asleep by the time we reached the flat.

She slept on and off for days, and when she was done sleeping, she couldn't sleep any more. I'd wake early to find her not there; sometimes she'd walk through the early morning markets. Sometimes she'd be sat at the kitchen table all night, in pain, smoking, drinking tea, thinking about what we should do to get out. On the third day after the operation she admitted to heroin cravings. I couldn't tell her how hard I'd been battling all the days since we last used. I'd been taking double my dose of Subutex to cope with the withdrawal, and would run out before the week was up and go back into withdrawal. When I ran out this time I told her I'd have to score, and she didn't have to tell me she'd have to have some too. You can't use in the same flat as someone recovering from addiction; the cruelty of it alone makes it impossible to square with yourself.

I bathed her, washed her hair over the side of the bath, and sponged her body in a half-full bath, avoiding her dressing. Her breast was still there, swollen and extremely bruised. The bruises turned from yellow to purple to green. The smaller breast became the bigger breast and she winced every time someone walked by her in the street. She said the illness had made her feel vulnerable; that she could walk through Stoke Newington before she was ill, knowing she could fight if someone attacked her, but when she started to feel ill and the lump grew she would walk with her arm over the breast and feel as though she was fair game for any would-be rapist. She said she felt like that most of her life, but cocaine helped her walk around feeling like she could fight her way out of it, and she had. Only a month before we met, a kickboxer in a pub had followed her home and forced her to touch his hard-on in a dimly-lit street, and every time she pulled her hand away and said no, he forced her again, and told her he could "take" her, and looked into her eyes and said, "the look in your face." She had fought him off and they'd been interrupted by a passing stranger, but she said she spent the weeks after trying to find out where he lived so she could burn his house down.

I didn't have to ask her why she didn't go to the police. She'd been wanked over in a hotel bathroom, forced to the ground, she'd had her drink spiked in a pub and was raped by her "rescuer." Three assaults in one year, and she had been using drugs before each of them. A single white female, going out drinking alone, doing drugs alone, and she despised the police almost as much as she despised her attackers.

We lay in bed in the early hours, both thinking the same thing, and the counter-intuitive idea that co-existed with it: we needed to get out of London before it collapsed on us, or collapsed us entirely, and if we couldn't, then we'd use. I told her we'd get out and I'd get rid of my numbers, and she said she could get work somewhere and we could have a life, a place to ourselves, somewhere affordable. And we decided we'd get cats, too. Ginger cats. A rocking chair, we'd read poetry in bed and keep everything clean.

Ten *Don't Sell It, Don't Give It Away*

Hammersmith, 5th October, 1999, the year Florence became a teenage mother. We were seventeen and would not meet for almost two more decades. I was in the basement of my uncle's flat on a single bed next to a bay window. I had dreamed of a train derailing and killing dozens of London commuters. My uncle walked in like Buck Mulligan in his dressing gown and turned the radio on. There was a dead mouse stinking across the room in a mouse trap. On an ordinary day we'd go to his volunteer job by the studio where they filmed TFI Friday, see people like Danny Baker, go to the pub or the library or the launderette. He was a nutcase. I wasn't doing anything but avoiding going home to my mother's house.

The radio was faint and I began to speak but my uncle hushed me – we listened to the report as it came over the airways. A train had derailed at Ladbroke Grove killing thirty-one people and injuring more than four hundred. I told my uncle the dream. We drank tea, smoked a joint and walked over to the launderette to see our friend from Uzbekistan.

He remarked several times about my hacking cough, said I should smoke more weed to get the shit off my chest and that it was driving him mad, listening to it at night. Weeks later we worked out he was poisoning me with fly killer in the plug socket that buzzed and emitted a disgusting poison which caused the cough and might have killed me.

While I was in the same flat, the year 2000, the IRA blew up Hammersmith Bridge and I felt it in my sleep. The flash came through the walls and I sat upright with palpitations. It was 4.30 am and I felt that I was already dead.

*

Fabric, 2003. I was living on Cambridge Heath Road. It was summer, I was wearing a string vest, no coat, which I was prone to doing, walking around alone drinking beer in the street. I was trying to chat up a Japanese girl in the club. She seemed scared of me; her English wasn't good, I was on ecstasy and in the bathroom I caught sight of myself in the string vest and thought to myself, "she probably thinks I'm mad." Of course I was mad, I think.

I looked up from where I'd found myself in the club alone and saw my friends walk by me. Then I saw them walk by me again, from the same direction, slightly faster, as though the whole world had rewound itself and was playing over and over, with absolutely no conclusion, no end.

I was studying for an English Literature degree, living above a Chinese restaurant, suffering from marijuana psychosis. I would break into building sites just to break things. There was no cause nor reason, nor particular effect. I bought a balaclava one day and walked down the street wearing it, watching people look at me in fear. Things happened without my volition twenty-four hours of every day and nothing I did changed any of it. I found myself dealing with a forty-odd-year-old male Irish stalker after falling flat on my face and splitting my lip. A young Muslim woman picked me up off the street with my two shopping bags covered in blood, as blood gushed in perfectly timed rivulets, upwards, towards my nose and eyes; I swallowed it back down through my nose and couldn't believe the mess it was creating. Everything at that time was outside of me, and I was only ever-so-slightly there.

I took myself to A&E and the Irish man at the desk watched me put the blood-stained shopping bags in the bin. Immediately afterwards two smackheads came and took them out and walked off with my blood-covered shopping and the man behind the desk appeared concerned and friendly, with a hint of familiarity I later came to understand was the standard demeanour of infatuated stalkers. Somehow, he got my number and asked me for a drink. No matter how many times I rebuked him, he called. He asked me what he'd done, why I wouldn't go; the pleading became threatening, and I stopped answering my phone to anyone. I sat around in my string vest smoking weed and contemplating some kind of ending – a conclusion, to me, to all things. My brain went out too far and even the sky at night and all its glorified suns terrified me.

In later years I discovered the reason I felt strange as a child. My mother had smoked a lot of weed, like I had always thought all adults did. If they did it all day long, that was normal. My uncle told me she would put weed in my food as a baby. Every time I was stoned, after I had processed this non-event, this undisclosed trauma, I receded into a wan, half-ghost.

*

My uncle always told me my mood affected the weather. I was staying with him in Birmingham in my late twenties. We went for a long drive and every time the weather dipped or darkened he told me it was because my mood was low. We spoke endlessly of time and the universe, music theory, Hegel, premonitions. He took so much acid he said he didn't feel like himself unless he was tripping.

He told me he was the sixth most intelligent person in the world. He said, "don't use heroin until you're in your thirties." It was advice I took too literally. I never told him I had discovered it. He always said I didn't need drugs, that I was naturally trippy.

I inherited his Martin when he died. I played the strings until they were completely dull, and I couldn't change them. The strings tied around in curlicues at the top of the fretboard. I think

DMT killed him, but no one could confirm how he died. I flogged a lot of his things for smack. I often thought he wouldn't have minded, or more often than that, I didn't care.

My uncle developed a love for animals in later life and said the two cats he brought over from New Jersey taught him how to love. We once found an injured swan on a canal towpath, feathers around it in an obscene pattern of nature's work. We called the RSPCA and three boys on dirt bikes drove up and began revving their engines to scare it out of the towpath so they could ride on. We called the police, they left; the swan stayed motionless, occasionally hissing at us, but unthreateningly, out of fear. My uncle stared at it for a half hour before the RSPCA inspector came and congratulated us on doing the right thing. It wasn't really hurt, just in shock. We walked away and it seemed as though the whole scene behind us dissolved in an instant. I could hear the swan's hiss in my sleep. Maybe it was the poisonous fly-killer plug-in that so often interrupted my dream sequences with eerie noises and apocalyptic scenarios that never really ended or climaxed. I slept where mice died horribly in wooden mousetraps, where flies wouldn't dream of going, where swans didn't die or do anything other than lie and wait.

Eleven *Mean Old World*

When I moved out of a squat in Islington in 2015, I was officially homeless. I tried to ring the guy who had let me into the house to give him £20 worth of drinks down the pub but he never answered his phone. I was deep into smack and through winter I lived without heating in a flat that would've made most people vomit, sleeping on a camp bed in my coat, with my hat on. Someone had painted the windows shut. I spent Christmas Day there, smoking heroin and crack, listening to a digital radio. If I topped up the meter, it'd take off a third of the money instantly for all the debt the guy had racked up. He was using all his money on drugs; a rich family kept his addictions funded, but he paid for nothing.

I usually wouldn't have been up at ten in the morning, but the day I was evicted the bailiffs knocked on the door and I was already up, figuring out how much I'd need to score and how much I could afford. I opened the door and the bailiffs seemed surprised I answered; they were with the manager of the estate who was reasonable with me; we'd been in touch days before as he was in court over mobile phone fraud, he'd admitted to me. He'd got involved with a gang on the estate who were getting him to sign for expensive mobile phones then flogging them. I'd been in court the day before for a stay of eviction and had seen him; it hadn't been granted. He seemed to care about the fact I'd been fucked about, and told me that although I had ten minutes to get my stuff and leave, he'd let me back in to get the rest of it.

I grabbed the things that were worth most: my Stratocaster, a borrowed violin in an old wooden case, and a bag of things on my back. I walked out in the pissing rain and went straight to Islington Town Hall to tell them I was homeless. They handed me an appointment for two weeks' time. I walked to see the guy who had got me evicted and banged on his parents' door. He opened up, looked at the ground and said, "sorry, but they lied to me."

I told him I'd stay in his parents' one-and-a-half-million-pound house for a few days and that he had no choice. So I hauled my stuff in, took one of the spare bedrooms and refused to interact with him until I left. One night, a friend took me out to a steakhouse and the guy who just made me homeless again texted me, asking me if I wanted some chips. My friend commented on the audacity of a man who could fuck my life up, make me homeless, but offer me chips as compensation.

*

I began my relationship with heroin in 2013 with reckless abandon and absolute commitment. I had two friends, the guy who made me homeless and Cee, who I'd requested to bring some for me. I genuinely wanted to be addicted to it. Cee kept coming over, saying it was shit and she'd smoked it, and my junkie "landlord" kept failing to meet me, making excuses. Cee turned up at my flat at that time and had brought the desired objects: a couple of bags of smack, maybe fifteen pounds' worth. She left and I used it on my own. At first it made me quite hyper; I vomited and listened to the Allman Brothers' *At Fillmore East.* It's impossible to ask a heroin addict why they continued, or why they fell in love with it so much. You might as well ask them where it hurts and why they needed to work so hard to numb the pain. I wanted to forget the answer to that question, and therein I became a junkie.

Within a week I had five dealers' numbers, including a black guy I met at Cee's. He came round my flat and made me smoke it in front of him. He was a highly suspicious and paranoid dealer, and called Cee after he left me thinking I was a cop. After a few months of scoring from him, he expressed an interest in moving in with me. I had to walk him around, stoned, showing him my mostly empty home. My enthusiasm seemed to make him back off – I often found he seemed to forget I was a junkie and he was my dealer, since his usual clientele were probably absolute scum.

He walked into my place once and I asked for "6B and 3 white" and he shushed me and told me not to say it like that. He gestured to the ceiling and told me there were cameras. Sometimes we'd have to pretend he was a guitar student of mine, and I'd write my request on a piece of paper and he'd leave saying loudly, "yeah, don't worry, I'm a good learner," then return with the goods. I saw him for about a year and a half, then he stopped being convenient as dealers on council estate stairwells offered better deals. He stupidly imagined there was more to our relationship than my need for drugs.

If I went into withdrawal, it would cease the second I knew I'd scored. Someone had once told me that heroin is only physically, not psychologically addictive. The withdrawal scares any junkie – the unmanageable pain and the "terrors" that so many spoke about. But nothing to me was more horrifying than the thought that I'd have to feel every single emotional pain or abuse I'd ever suffered, all over again, with no buffer and no relief.

Twelve *Idiot Waltz*

Returning to our attic room in South Tottenham I caught myself saying, "hi honey, I'm home!" I arrived to find her draped across the bed, smiling, and it struck me I hadn't used that word in many years; I had no concept of what "home" was. Home is a word with connotations of warmth, happiness and safety. Having a home brings about a sense of what it would be to lose it. For those who never really had one, then find themselves experiencing it for the first time in adulthood, the fear of losing it is more potent than the relief it brings to have it.

We didn't have a cooker and couldn't use the downstairs kitchen because of the landlady's dogs, their shit, and having witnessed a mouse climb out of the toaster I vowed never to use it again. Florence bought us a slow cooker and made three-day stews or Mexican dishes that she would adapt and change, so one day we might have a chicken stew, but it would eventually become a risotto. I'd lived off nutrition drinks and the occasional two-in-the-morning pastry so it was an extreme luxury to eat cooked meals. We had a microwave my friend stole and hid at my place, and we used it to breathe warmth into things and make hot chocolate at night. She'd go out to the shops in her Jewish housewife dresses and come back laden with bargain foodstuffs and the occasional plate or cup, then set about cleaning the room and making it "princess."

She would wash our clothes and clean the floor, drape fairy lights and hang our clothes in the wardrobe, not just pile them on the floor and sniff them before wearing, as had been my prior method. The landlady continued to refer to her as "my friend," but we spent more and more time in the attic, not going downstairs or interacting with the other housemates. This only made them more eager to know what was going on, and things often went missing from our room; food, things they thought we wouldn't miss. The rest of the house was a constant intrusion, not only into our living space, but also our mental space. Even during the periods where we didn't use smack, we'd start fucking only to find that we were put off by the noises downstairs, our other housemate whistling or shouting instead of talking to someone in the same room, or the sense that we were being listened to by several ears.

I'd run her a bath and fill it with bubbles and foam, but I'd have to clean it every single time, before I ran the taps. It seemed as though no matter what we did, the grime and scum would rise to the surface immediately. I'd sit on a fold-out chair and watch her bathe, reading her Gogol and smoking cigarettes next to the bathtub while a senile black cat clambered in and out of the bathroom window meowing soundlessly. She'd smoke in the bath and we'd have to keep talking to a minimum to prevent being overheard. I couldn't imagine having to live like that with her for years. It was as though I had her completely and could only access part of her and her desires, her life, her joy, and only when everyone in the house conveniently left and we knew we were completely alone.

Drugs never left our minds or our daily existence, even when we weren't using. If we walked anywhere, we could both pick out several places we'd scored. Our tendencies towards automatically looking out for these places, or gravitating towards them, left us feeling uneasy if we strayed from our patch – having a geographical map to keep our dependency in one space didn't help us rid ourselves of it. It held us in tightly. We lived at the absolute centre of a world in which immediate cessation of pain was always possible. You can't get away from that. You have to be a long way from it; the whole world is full of drugs and addicts, so you have to leave it *for* something else you want more, or *with* what is left to salvage.

The saving grace of the attic room was being able to watch the sunrise and sunset from the huge window at the back of the room. We'd often leave the dusty, maroon velvet curtains open, so the light would come in and wake us. I often think about how the sun is a more sensible thing to worship than a God. She often spoke about how she went to NA, but all the talk about her "higher power" and the applause she'd receive for basically admitting to huge errors of judgment and wanton self-destruction made her feel far worse, so she stopped going and returned to the safety of addiction. She said there were worse things than a drug addict – "a community of drug addicts!" she always added.

The sun is at least a real object that provides us with vitality and the means to live. I've had far too many experiences of drugs and being high to recall them, but I remember so many sunrises and sunsets. Looking out over Cornwall in my childhood, I felt a sense of the safety and reliability of the turning of each day. When our days and rhythms began to coalesce, waking and sleeping at the same time no matter what strange time of day or night that was, I felt a sense that there were cycles, that things progressed, changed, continued, and that I was held in place by something, not permanently untethered and disconnected.

I would often sleep curled around her back; being only slightly taller than her I could curl my whole self around and into her and had for the first time experienced *rest*. The sense that I protected her, and that it was only the sun that woke us up and told us when it was best to sleep, kept us in a kind of semblance of routine and stability. On the few days she had to go somewhere or leave, I often sat feeling as though there was nothing I could do. As though the sun had risen or set in the wrong place, or time had shifted, or the attic had warped into something other than a real, safe space. I sometimes went to the pub and drank with old friends, but did nothing but talk about her, imagining the dark crowding in on the room, curling around her like another body.

We had to fend off our pasts from entering the room we lived in. Our phones often went unanswered or stayed on silent. If we spoke about things that we'd endured it was while we were caning smack, and then afterwards we could return to the wonderful, ever-sunny beach that was our ever-rolling existence of numbing and sinking. We spoke about places we wanted to go, and things we wanted to do. She wanted to ride ponies on beaches in Iceland; I wanted to travel to Italy and see the architecture and art; but we didn't speak about them as though they were ambitions, or as though they were pipedreams. We spoke about all reality as though it was only one hair's breadth removed from actual experience.

Just to get out of the place we'd head down into Stoke Newington and Dalston looking for charity-shop books and clothes. I'd head to the nearest pub while she riffled through endless racks of cheap clothes, and she'd often find me, excited about something she'd picked up for me; a designer shirt for £1, a pair of shoes for £2. I'd have a pint of cider ready for her, and we'd walk back with fish and chips or just find another pub, or walk through a park in the sun, watching all the middle-class mothers call their children or park expensive prams while we drank out of bottles and cans on the lawn, watching the sun begin to turn and fade.

It was a peaceful way of living, with or without heroin. We'd always buy enough smack so as not to have to score soon afterwards, and have a two-day stretch holed up, occasionally going for a walk, listening to blues songs and talking. On heroin, we ate little; off it we fucked, drank and filled our stomachs with actual food.

During a clean period, we took a train to Manchester where Florence was born. She laughed at how terrified I was of the trams, which seemed to emerge randomly and silently in the street. I couldn't understand why people weren't killed every day by them, marauding around where most people appeared to be drunk. We hit thrift shops, amazed to find they were unaffordable, compared with Dalston and small London boroughs. There were more homeless people, and she pointed out the posh-looking hotels where you'd only go "for a nasty blowjob."

At Manchester museum we practically skipped into the dinosaur exhibition of fossils, bones, timelines of pre-historic pasts. Sea monsters and murals writhed below the eyeline as it gravitated towards the T-Rex at the foot of the hall. I thought about how unlikely it was any of it was real. I thought about how inane a thought that was to have. Then I imagined that none of it was, while my heart tried to grip back onto its bloodflow.

She said that walking around with me was like walking around with a child in constant awe and wonder. She often had to place her hand on my back to guide me away from an object jutting out or a car, a lunatic or a strutting, single-minded businessman. We went to Night and Day café, she was excited to show it to me, but all I could really tell her was, "I can't stand that Manchester guitar. I can't really believe I came to Manchester and there really are those bands around." We walked into places where The Smiths and Joy Division were playing. Manchester seemed like a kind of parody of itself, with all the same gentrification problems as London. She spoke fondly of the Northern Quarter, before it had become "98% hipster" and on one street alone I spotted four handlebar moustaches and a plethora of men in ankle-grazing slacks and thick, black-framed *intelligentsia* spectacles. I spotted every smackhead on the streets from a ten-yard radius. She told me the smack had always been best in Manchester. I immediately replied, "let's not live here then."

In her more cogent moments, Florence avidly described places she'd been in her twenties with her ex-husband, her son, and said we should save money, go away places and travel. We'd agree to it, and talk for hours about where to go, making elaborate plans, googling for cheap deals on rental and train tickets, but then forty-eight hours later or less, some kind of traumatic event would be rekindled. Something new would confront us, like a text from her ex, or a letter from the council, or worse news from her consultant about her condition, and the only plan that made sense would be for me to go out and score. We were professional achievers in terms of stopping, but in terms of starting again we would throw ourselves in and dive until we reached the very bottom. In little under forty-eight hours we could use £180 or more of heroin. All plans laid to waste, there was nothing more to do then score more. It's impossible to explain to someone who has never been hooked on smack that no matter what you think you want, no matter what kind of future you imagine for yourself, it no longer features when you are an addict, in fact it doesn't even exist. The possibility of any futures without smack don't matter. If you think at all you think in the same way you dream – disconnected, floating in a miasma of perpetual bliss *in the now.*

Turning to Camus this morning, I reread the passage at the end of *The Outsider* which begins, "I looked up at the mass of stars and signs in the night sky and laid myself open for the first time to the benign indifference of the world. And finding it so much like myself, in fact so fraternal, I realized that I'd been happy, and that I was still happy."

Holding my own addiction together in the grander remit of my own brief and uncelebrated life was reassuringly simple - though holding together the addictions of two people was ultimately eroding my sense of self. Even my sense of time failed as I watched Florence drift in and out of a deep opiate sleep which is never wholly unconscious. She would fall asleep holding my hand, or with her hand on my chest, her breathing deep and often interrupted by pauses to murmur or cough, or whimper. Then it was less like a dreamscape and more as though I was watching nothing more than a nightmare overcome her, with me doing nothing more than observing it while it carried her away. The heroin stood at the door to our attic room and looked me square in the face as though to say, "it's me or her." But conversely, I spoke back and offered the truer alternative, "it's *you* or her." It wasn't so much a choice, to send the one away and keep the other to myself, as an understanding that that was what I must do. Eventually, always eventually. On heroin, everything can always wait another day.

Then I would see heroin stood at the door, nodding for her to come over. He could take her from me quietly and quickly, leave me gazing into the ashtray with soot all over my hands.

She would ask me every now and then if I loved heroin more than I loved her. I could easily, immediately respond in the negative. I did not. But she would never ask me to stop using, or maintaining her addiction by agreeing to score, and using myself. Any complaint she made about heroin would denounce the natural order in her world. Take it away, and she was left with herself. Take me away and she was left with nothing. But she wanted to keep us both.

There would have to be an incentive to wean her off. It would have to be better than heroin. She had no interest in money or possessions, she didn't want for much and didn't ask for anything. I had no money and no stable means of providing for her. But if I spoke about love, or asked her about what meant most to her, the answer was there, but unutterable. She had already lost the few things she loved most and she wanted to return to her son so much she was afraid to even speak of it. She often told me, "hope is a terrible thing. If you have none, and do not try to cultivate any, you can't lose."

PART II

FLORENCE

The last London sunset was nothing to celebrate. It was neither mournfully enjoyable nor beautiful. Sat in a smoke nest together eating tasteless noodles and drinking Ribena, and one more forced stage exit to go, I found a bottle of champagne we were supposed to drink to celebrate being clean, but never felt sure enough that we were, or would ever be, to actually drink it – green and dust-coated, sticky with nicotine; no reflection in the glass.

I drank from the bottle while Morgan took a bath in the stinking bathroom caked in other peoples' shit and sucked up spilled bubbles from all the prancing around manic trying to think of the concluding dress to my London life. A flocked red halter-neck dress with a tutu looked stupid. I am old, or something like that. You can see the scars, scars upon scars upon scars upon tender parts I'd rather not expose anymore. M. arrived at the foot of the stairs to our noir attic and couldn't raise a smile for the exquisite white vintage pleated gown. One breast was noticeably smaller than the other, with scars upon scars through the sheer cloth. Fucking hell. So I sucked the bubbles up, smoked a roll-up inexpertly and spat out the nasty yellow taste. I uttered, "I'm so attractive." The only deadweight left in the stinking pile of clothes appeared as a ghost beneath a tweed overcoat, mangled at the bottom of a bag we packed weeks ago to leave and didn't make it. White blouse, pleated back, dipped hem, open collar, tight black trousers and pissed out my face, we trotted to Seven Sisters and the world sped by like badly aimed darts, each fading like reality fades when you're underground and sick.

The tube was rammed at Tottenham Court Road. My psycho-geographical map of London is just all the places I have scored or fallen asleep wasted. One time I scored in some shabby wine bar nearby after one hour of sleep in four days and walked for miles in £1 charity-shop sunglasses with a chronic nosebleed. I might have told someone I loved them that night but perhaps only because I needed money, drugs and affection, and I could not find money or drugs. Walking up to the escalator I saw a man with a flash of recognition in his expression; a mod jacket – I thought I could not possibly know anyone who might wear a mod jacket, but it was Manny and he was supposed to be going to the event I was performing at. I immediately changed from a pissed-up teetering recovering smackhead into the celebrated idiot I apparently was in real life and threw my arms around him disingenuously and rasped the word, "darling." He said he had to meet his girlfriend for dinner and added, "you did say you'd be late but this is very late. They're all waiting for you." I must have pulled a face like a sick monkey and replied, "I'm one bottle of champagne in, and they're all dicks. This isn't real life, is it?" It wasn't rhetorical. Morgan smiled at Manny in a kind of you-know-her way and Manny looked at Morgan in an I-now-have-to-go-and-meet-my-prissy-rich-girlfriend-for-oysters-or-some-hipster-junk way, and I said, "I don't have to go, do I?" to which they both nodded. Manny seemed bewildered but not amused. "They all love you, isn't that great? Don't you enjoy that?" I had never considered I should.

Dan was waiting, doing all the audience foreplay for me. Two voluptuous women came over to introduce themselves and I immediately requested two "supersize" drinks. I couldn't have been more of a cunt, and it only occurred to me halfway through the set that Morgan had never seen me onstage before. I told the audience a rather notorious poetry publisher was a "massive cunt" and yelled some slurred abuse at a group of upper-class Klingons by the bar for shouting something out at my friend Dan. I managed the audience by making them so tense and offended they had to believe they liked me.

And K turned up and expected me to be hopelessly available.

I made it clear I was stringently unavailable and insulted his seven-foot-tall friend who I ordered to get on his knees to speak to me. The friend took this rather badly due to the onset of emasculating feelings. Momentarily the next morning I also recalled having told the audience, "I've suffered so you don't have to!" This wasn't a memory I met with horror; my judgement never needed to be sharp when performing. I consider all of it a circus full of people so psychologically bent out of shape I realised early on I could be anything as long as I *had* them. But then reality blurs, and not just for the audience who only want me to be that way always, day and night, so they could believe someone could fall so far off the wagon and still gloriously exist. And sometimes I believed it was really me articulating words and sounds when in fact I know I have a higher understanding of meaning than I ever deployed in a room full of ticket-paying imbeciles with little or no grasp of language but a sense of where it might be cool to say you'd been when you meet up for drinks at the weekend.

I began to wonder if there was nothing I couldn't learn to hate well.

*

Several mornings I woke early, sat bolt upright and said the words, "I cannot be here." We rarely got up before the crack of evening and we did our shopping at the local twenty-four-hour shop late at night or in the early hours. We filled gallon bottles of water to use in the attic so as not to have to use anything associated with the other housemates who were each insane, members of cults, cocaine-addicted, poor and badly hiding the fact that they were each seething with hatred for one another. We had our routine, and we loved, and we lay and we spoke and we lived but we also stank.

We were in a heavy and deep drift. Footsteps swelled into

potholes, into pools, into wasteland, treading into open territory, and prickles up the spine when a dealer walks by. Hand in hand, a five-finger discount and a skinfull, a whim turned into a three-day binge into a five-day binge into an addiction. Every phase of addiction felt different. A familiar drug became a new thing, a new affliction, a new taste, a new craving. Never quite the same as you remember, sometimes better, sometimes sadly lacking. Always better than this endless clarity some of us are cursed with, always.

*

There was a roasting hot Saturday in which we had the money to go see a theatre production of *Angels in America* being broadcast live at the Brixton Ritzy and I put on my floral cotton bandeau dress, my tits hitched up and preventing a view of my own feet; we caught the train and arrived only five minutes late for the showing. Two hours in, we took a break and left the theatre, with only a few pounds left and the day having been hugely frivolous for two people who equate any sum of money to the corresponding value of street drugs. We had a burger each from McDonald's, came back to the theatre and assumed our seats. Morgan had removed both plimsoles and socks and I began to attack the burger when a camp voice squealed, "David, make them go away! The smell! Oh god it's awful!" The man next to me leaned in and spat against my neck, "that's disgusting!"

"Oh, it really is," I replied, and took a hefty mouthful close to his face.

"David! Get them away from me! They *stink*!"

I finished the burger and loudly orated: "if I see either of those dickheads outside this theatre I am going to smash their faces in."

The camp voice continued for at least five minutes until he

was liberally shushed. The last thing he said was, "didn't you smell them? They smelled like *pigs*. They shouldn't have been allowed into a theatre." (It was not a slow education, being a working-class girl from the North in London. The road ahead is paved thus: if you must continue with your uncouth accent you will be patronised and condescended. If you must attempt to be completely authentic to yourself do not expect to find work or for men to find you attractive. There are plenty of bimbos whose accents have been redefined to the most basic, charisma-less RP, who can keep their mouths shut, have an adequate typing speed, look good in office clothes and put out. You are an orifice. You will be treated as an orifice. Millions of others don't complain.)

There was something so ineffably dreadful about the two men in the theatre that we went straight to the pub to smoke and drink and a helpless death-like demoralised feeling rose awkwardly on noticing how many men in the bar were staring at my tits. Having Morgan point it out to me, I knew the best course of action was to contrive a way to score some smack. Sweet, juicy smack.

It was never that easy. Morgan had been a very successful addict for several years. For Morgan to slip up would be to do it in full consciousness and acceptance of the decision. Making a decision for two was easier for me. I had to be extremely clever. I had to convince Morgan that either I couldn't live without it at that point and would suffer unbearably, that we would both be better off stoned that particular day or night or morning or afternoon. Sometimes it would take several hours to get my point to connect, but the moment we made that decision, every single action or thought from that point was a rush to get what we needed. It became a team effort; I would procure the bacofoil, clipper lighters, tobacco and drinks, and Morgan would retrieve the money from the ATM, make the call and take the trip into Hackney or down the road and wait around anxiously to deal with some crazed, dipshit crackhead who was heavily paranoid. I'd have the bacofoil ready; two rectangular pieces, I'd make two tubes with the foil on a knife sharpener and cut one end clean, and have lighters ready, water in the kettle, the tobacco and ashtray on the bedside table, newspaper to place the foils on after they've been used so the black marks don't stain everything, and baby wipes, which were highly essential though not always affordable. When Morgan returned with our bounty there would be no need for conversation, or maybe there'd be a flustered and excited story about the dealer and some stupid shit they'd pulled, but focus would not stray from the unwrapping of the first bag and placing equal amounts on both pieces of tinfoil in the fold I made previously. And then we'd pick our lighters because I needed a smaller flame so as not to burn it all, while Morgan needed a bigger flame, and then we'd begin.

An hour became several hours became several days. Ashtrays overflowed, dirty cups mounted up, less light in the room than darkness, and music: Elmore James, Howlin' Wolf, nightfall after nightfall. If we had to go out after the first few days, the sun would sting our eyes and we'd shake and stumble down the road to the train station to head to Dalston for Morgan's script or to the doctor so they could check out my obscene lump in my breast for the hundredth time and I could procure codeine.

I sometimes asked myself what it was I wanted and it might begin with things like being with Morgan forever, getting hitched perhaps, finding a house to live in? But those were junkie fantasies and seconds later the answer was lucidly clear and no other ambition could find its way through my opiate brain after I'd realised it: I wanted a lifetime supply of heroin, nothing more. I wanted not to have to degrade myself or stoop to get it; I wanted it all day every day and at night and that was the most humane existence I could imagine. It felt unfair that I couldn't have it, as it would make everything bearable, and this was a thought I have had far too often. I just wasn't sure whether it was what I essentially wanted most or whether it was in fact what I most needed.

After days or weeks stoned, there would be a day where we decided it was best to open the curtains and attempt to clean up. Morgan would always remember being told by another junkie there is less bacteria in your room if you let a lot of daylight in because daylight kills bacteria, and on announcing this we would open the heavy velvet curtains on the back window overlooking the back gardens of Hassidic Jew families. Children with sun in their hair, in their ringlets, mum and dad pushing kids on a swing, mummy pegging out washing. We'd stand and watch for a time, a darkness creeping into our thoughts until, entirely clouding them, without so much as a word to each other, we would return to the bed which was behind a second curtain, a nest; we would take up our instruments of choice, our heroin, and we would retreat until it became viable to exist again.

Sometimes in the rush we'd talk over each other, through each other and out of each other's thoughts. Sometimes Morgan would speak and I would speak and neither of us would know who said which thing or if we would ever remember the revelation we had at midnight. There was more point to this kind of talk than any other. It happened somewhere else in us – articulated, spoken, but heard in a different way, not via language.

We mined each other for answers and ideas. We didn't need to remember them – we lived in the moment of acceptance and awe, each astounded at being alive at all, and by the hours that revealed more broken bones and memories like tumours that sucked on the darkness and yes, sometimes we'd cry, and hold each other. We would promise one another we'd never separate if we couldn't fuck because of the smack; we would roll around in each other's bodies until we were wet through with sweat and we knew everything there was to know and no less than everything. *Everything* cannot and need not be articulated but can be comprehended when high. Plainly, the most deranged and pure of all truths was the knowledge and acceptance of the finite vastness of our human lives. There were too many things language did not reach, and we mined them and catalogued them all together. There were no names for these things and the more things-with-no-name we discovered the less we spoke, and the less we mourned, and the more the world was filled with them, so that a graveyard at three in the afternoon on the way to score was a delight that could not be described, and we had no need to describe things to one another in the way that people do and that we used to.

I cut most people out. There was no sense in anything friends said. Family was a misshapen ideal, an idea at best, and we had no affiliation with it. We avoided the landlady, the people we knew who had seen us daily before; the people in bars, the acquaintances, the close friends, the allies; human contact was in fact avoidable if we had each other – a different kind of "contact." Other people breached the parameters of our acceptance too regularly; we patched over the holes and dug in deeper. Their words and ideas were like batches of bad smack that we had no choice but to use but that we wished was the pure stuff that made things heavenly. To each other, we were the pure stuff. There was no need to water anything down by letting mediocrity in.

It's much easier to tell when someone is stoned over the phone than in person; to hide it well enough around people is part of the profession. It just takes so much energy, and that's why junkies prefer their own company or the company of their own kind. I always knew if Morgan was stoned when we spoke over the phone. I didn't always catch on in the secretive times in between our addiction phases. Morgan used and lied about it. Understanding this meant that I knew when to turn off my phone or not answer calls if I didn't want to know the truth about how my love was deceiving me.

Heroin allowed me to cut it all away to what I could bear.

So often I can't bear it. The world is so hostile now, I feel sure some time in my twenties I awakened into a world that is so consumed by hate and hostility that in my consciousness I become the centre of that. The blame and the responsibility lies with me; it's easier to turn it inside than keep it out. Someone demands this, someone wants that; if it's someone's fault, I've always been able to erase myself and take up the slack. I had a belief once that my actions could be important. Maybe my thoughts and the things I knew could be articulated in such a way that all the other bullshit would be drowned out by them; I'd be central to myself. Then one day I had to go and perform a monologue at an event full of the brightest and best London literati, and I was choosing a dress from the measly two-hooks-on-the-back-of-a-door-in-a-box-room wardrobe I had created from £1 charity shop sale crap, and just as though the whole world had changed from bright to lightless, I knew I should not go. My landlady was going to escort me there and watch the performance and I told her I could not go. I locked myself in the bathroom putting make-up on and scraping it off again, panicking until my face was red raw and she banged on the door and shouted, "you have to come, they're all waiting for you!" and I pulled my hair and began to hyperventilate then through the pressure and the craziness of unwillingness in my body and mind, I suddenly found myself leaving the room and picking up my coat as she tailed along and told me I'd look a lot nicer if I didn't have that anxious expression on my face.

Is there any point in describing what happened next? My cleavage was showing, my dress was too tight, I drank out of anxiety. I asked for help to get home, but everyone left one by one and in the daze of finding my way I was followed into a hotel bathroom. I remember fingernails, blood in my mouth, nausea, bodily pressure, trying to drown out the noise as I did as a child, giving up, saying "stop," my floor-length dress going into the toilet bowl, wet through, sinking to the floor and him finishing by wanking in my face telling me his sick thoughts. He had been watching all night. He had known he was going to do it before I arrived, my body told me so.

I staggered to a tube station I didn't know where and saw my streaked make-up in the reflection of a shop window which was closed as it was around two am and I saw blood on my cheek and tried to find a doorway to roll a cigarette away from the relentless rain but my hands didn't work anymore and my feet wouldn't go. I knew I couldn't walk or run; I would fall into the street or the road in horror. Some parts felt numb, others smarted, and my mind became a channel for all the hostile noise the world had to make, it just didn't stop. A black cab came by slowly, so slow it was frightening, and I hailed it without even thinking, got in, and even though I looked like I did, like I'd just been assaulted, the driver attempted to make amiable conversation with me. I got out half a mile before I reached my flat. An ATM was right beside me. I recall a number and a withdrawal and a long wait in a side street and a short drive in a big black car I had to fight to get out of, and an open bar and a few lines and my own hideous face in the silent child's box room where I slept like a person who did not know they were alive or human. I might have been just an image at that point; an image being intercepted or seen by someone else, transmitting the image to somewhere else, so far removed from my own heart I really was dead.

Can you imagine what the whole world sounded like the next day? It screamed fuck you! Every mouth, face, every expression, every cuss, every blow to the arm by a passing stranger, every shitty email I could not answer if I tried, every man hanging around waiting for a bus to take them off to the outer-stellar galaxies of dipshit misery. I had to have my laptop fixed to write. I had spilled milk on it in the anxiety of the previous afternoon trying to line my stomach and calm my nerves and the technician at the shop said, "it's dead."

So I called my husband. Separated, burned, but not estranged at that time, there was no one else to reach. I did not breathe a word of the truth that time. I just breathed, listened and said things distant to my own mind. He asked me what I wanted after three minutes of that; I said I missed him, which I had never felt or said before. He said he didn't have time for that now; he said he hadn't cared about me for years and wasn't going to start now. The woman he had an affair with was in the room breathing hostile green pangs of unreality into my head and egging him on to verbally murder me. "Go and tell someone else," he said. "Someone who gives a shit."

So many times I've been sure it could not possibly get worse, and every single time it did. Then it did again, and again. I've either clawed it back or am in Hell, most hours I feel that is my truth. I can never be sure which it'll be from hour to hour: just about there and coping, or completely consumed by pain – reality only bent back into shape on smack. It bent so perfectly into shape that I understood what I was and it did not need to be articulated.

Three *Make Me A Pallet On Your Floor*

Being with Morgan at first was like being cocooned in a perfectly spherical, permeable shell or bubble and inside the bubble was the best afternoon of your life with the best person and it would be perfect and forever if you could only not have to waste most of the hours fending off the million entities trying to break in and invade and poison it. It was like shunning *life itself as you knew it* to be in the reality you chose as truth but always having to vigilantly defend it to within an inch of your sanity. Our hopeless inner cries were ones of please-leave-us-alone. Pains beneath the ribs, in the heart and chest, one breast dying of premature motherhood and its untimely death by the intervention of patriarchal lies and the other stood to attention in love. I was just one big tit being bitten, chewed and mutilated before. Now I was a whole being with one good tit. We were on our own *a kind.* Our bodies were not a series of functions, needs and obligations. It was like emerging from death with your twinned soul and both of you seeking a bright and varied void in which there was no hostility, no pain and no need of anything but its continuity in perpetuum.

If you feel I'm over-romanticising then you've never truly loved, or you've never been addicted to narcotics and truly in love, or neither, or both. Or you've not been me, or us. We may have been forgotten but we have already forgotten you – no face held any interest to us. No fear, flinching, gut-feeling, sense of impending doom – a daily reality we lived for years. Everything we had experienced became just something we described to each other when high and talking things through but neither of us could ever really be sure any of it happened. We only knew what we were and what we were in each other.

We were window panes that looked into rooms, that looked out over fields and into other rooms, into houses, into sheets of glass, into specks of dust, into cells and physical majesty, into nothing at all and we had never begun anywhere and if we shattered in turn then the universe we thought we were sure of would do a pirouette on a green lawn someplace east of hostility and move on to create an imbalance in a place where time had already lost and death was the only state of serenity and nothing at all could be imagined or unimagined, everything merely was.

It's impossible to be in the world now that I've spent time living so far beyond it.

*

Morgan was not part of the world as I had known it since childhood but was absolutely apart from it – a personified state of limbo between the physical and metaphysical world and the complacent reality of everyday living. Morgan did not just accept things as they were reported to be, endlessly inquisitive, a perceptiveness to marry mine so that we very often seemed to have the same idea simultaneously and there was no friction between our sensibilities. We were afraid of the potency of our love and it became entirely true, and still is true, that the only thing we have to fear is losing one another. We know unimaginable physical and emotional pain; we accept the complacent world of Heideggerian "essent" and waste and tragedy. If one of us died the other would only have heroin. It would not be enough. There would only be death to look for.

There was only one other being in the whole world I loved or could ever love and I had worked hard to not think of him for all the days we had been parted – my son. Aged ten, an instrument of god in heaven; after his father found someone younger and more benign and infinitely more ordinary and forced me to live in the attic of the sterile marital home until I feared I had gone mad, I had spent every penny I could earn travelling back to our son in the north, only to receive more abuse and experience more of the truth of the memories I had left behind in that terrible place. At first I stayed in the attic, but the last time I had been sat in the lounge crying late one night thinking his father was in the marital bed I had been pushed out of, when he walked into the room, saw me crying and dishevelled on the sofa, and simply walked into the kitchen, made a drink and walked past me and returned to the dead bed without uttering a word. It wasn't that he hadn't cared; it was the realisation that his behaviour was entirely normal and he would have behaved no differently as a man who still claimed to love me. I think that was the night the walls broke down – the lies I constructed and he constructed to keep me in check and preserve that house as such a fortress of untruth and toeing the line – and I remembered where he hid the key to the safe which was filled with boxes upon boxes of opiates he'd once been prescribed after an operation that went wrong, and didn't take though still stashed for some reason – I opened it, a trove; I began to take pills and they released me. In the morning he informed me that he'd sent our son to his mother's as he'd forgotten he'd arranged for him to go out with her, and it was the only day I could see him for a month – I'd paid over a hundred pounds for the train ticket and would now have to stay in the house I'd had to leave all weekend. Stunned and half-eaten by despair I took more pills and more pills and laid on the camp bed in the attic all day polluting the room with the occasional forbidden cigarette which plumed aggressively and spoiled what still felt clean. By evening he had grown sick of my presence and threw me out of the house. I took the train back to London high and nauseous in an empty carriage at midnight and scored by King's Cross station from a man who told me he loved Dostoyevsky and asked me if I'd have a gang bang with him because he loved MILFs. He asked me if I liked parties. He said he went to great parties where there were guys and lots of girls and the girls would be naked and the guys would fuck them all, all together, all night. He asked me if I liked gang bangs. I said it sounded complicated and tiring. He told me he wanted to take me out on a Monday, as he only had Mondays off, but guys rang in sick all the time and he had to cover. I told him he was a committed professional.

Soon there was no money and no work and my husband would call me out of the blue where I sat alone in my box room wondering how I could possibly go on. He'd just want to tell me how happy he was with his new blonde, pretty and inane girl-friend who had only just left her parents' and he would relish calling me a cunt. There was no real reason for it, and I knew he wished I would die to make his life flow more smoothly and get me out of his newly invented romantic landscape where the debris of my life could fossilise and remain buried beneath all the shiny new constructs he imagined in his head and his banal but fixed personal narrative.

Everywhere I walked I had to make myself into twenty different people or personas to cope at the altitude of being seen. I could make myself hard and mean just as quickly as you might switch on a light. I was so many different people that it was as though if I looked over my shoulder the real me would be far behind but visible, in rags, smoking, drunk, in shock, unseen, invisible. I avoided seeing her and coloured my distress with every shade of narcotic and every kind of liquor.

I thought: if only I had hidden myself completely before that marriage and had no witness to judge my pain or manipulate and enhance my grief. I thought: if only I wasn't so conscious of myself and saw the world in a grey opaque shimmer. I thought: if only I did not feel and could not love.

We were high when we made the decision to leave London and so the next day it seemed unlikely we should ever think it or say it again. I dared not ask Morgan if it were true that we could leave, that we would leave; if we never did, I would need more heroin and a shorter rope.

Morgan decided when it was time to do a withdrawal and I entered it with a thousand internet searches for somewhere else to be. We thought of Manchester but we hated it when we visited. It was a death trap of the ethically undecided and killer trams and people capable of killing themselves or others. We thought of Liverpool but the two cities were excellent drug ports in the north and could invite a new shame. I told Morgan, "the drugs are better but more expensive, it'd be suicide." It may or may not have been true but we had to construct as many reasons to stay straight as possible. We looked at Google maps and pin-pointed areas close to my son but far enough away not to have to live beneath the perpetual cloud my family's misery hung over the place I used to live and added a further ten-mile radius just to ensure it. I remember how when I was a child and we drove to my grandmother's, my mother would always say, "there's always an enormous grey cloud above *that* house." For many years I truly believed my family were an abyss that looked into you – psychogeographically polluting space and time. Morgan and I observed the shadow I drew over the area I could not return to, and we began to search for a house beyond the perimeter. I took pleasure in explaining the difference in house prices and rental prices in the north because I loved to see Morgan awestruck. Living poor in London for so long makes you forget living was possible without the constant threat of eviction or bloodloss.

We arrived just to the east of where we could bear to go, close enough to be with Joe, my son. I knew his father would not make it easy but without him we knew we would die young in a bed-sit in London and my heart would have been cold long before it stopped. We got on the train and as I was attempting to buy alcohol, Morgan patted me gently on the shoulder and I explained, "I had so many lonely journeys, I learned to drink." Morgan wanted to change, and to change I also had to change. The station shop was off-limits; I wasn't allowed to carry booze onto the train. I felt slightly ashamed of how far you can fight your sensible resistance to self-destruction until you normalise destroying yourself, so you no longer even ask yourself why you're doing it. Destroying myself was not at all frightening, it was welcome perhaps; loneliness frightened me, so did loss, but death was an ever-present comfort, as appalling as that sounds.

We'd made arrangements to view several houses over two days and the only hotel in the area took up the last money we had spare. I have no idea anymore how we came about funding our lives; the concerns we have now just did not concern us then: payments, bills, rent. If you are desperate or addicted you find it; you may look back and have no recollection of how, but what you despaired for and were driven towards found you just as fervently as you sought it. I called my husband from the train and explained that I was viewing houses to move back to the north to see Joe and he scoffed at first, then sounded alarmed. "I thought you had your happy *bohemian* life now in London," he sneered. I wrapped the conversation up as quickly as I could. I was going to move as soon as possible; I wanted to see Joe that evening if he would allow me to, at the hotel we were staying in, so I could tell him and so I could see him again. For some reason he relented from his position of making obstacles and waves of pain and we made brief arrangements and I hung up and breathed. The world breathed. Morgan held my hand and we held ourselves together with the heat of our blood and the kind of determination a junkie knows he owns if he can bear a withdrawal and truly wants what is there waiting on the other side.

For a time, we'd realise when at a counter or paying for a drink somewhere that our hands and nails were black and ugly and our pupils were pinned and no matter how we tried, we looked like smackheads. We knew we were seen as smackheads. We scratched ourselves and our skin was sallow and the weight fell off our bones. We felt in ourselves that we were the same intelligent, perceptive people we had always been; I had been admired as a writer and dramatist; I had a childish sense that these people who looked at us as though we were scum didn't know the truth about who we truly were and what we were truly capable of. Morgan's shoes had holes in them, I had junkie acne. Make-up put a bit of colour back into my face but there was so often a black mark on my cheek or brow I hadn't washed off or had failed to notice, or a burn hole in my clothes, or I stank of smoke and sweat and I couldn't hide it or pretend, so I didn't see friends anymore. I didn't dare go into most shops and establishments. It felt unjust, and it made me resent everyone I encountered if we did venture out in daylight. While the train rattled across the country I saw myself as clean, truly clean, and felt as though my brain had been wrapped in Egyptian linen and soaked in rose water and I had dressed well in clean clothes and this was a lot to be proud of. Morgan wore a peacoat and suit trousers and we smiled at one another while we were dressing, expressing the same wordless thought, "this is us now."

*

These days if you don't feel as though you're about to fall into the well any second never to return you are lucky. We embarked at Manchester Piccadilly station, hauled our luggage sweating in the July misery of merciless heat and left the station to smoke our pre-rolled. A man in the outdoor alcove to the station sat bleeding from the head with a sign that read, "punch me for money." There were dark clots around his nose and he had ashen skin and almost blue-tinged features, a bloated neck and stubble, and a bunch of louts walked past drunk discussing how they'd pay to punch someone. "Him?" one cunt enquired. "Any cunt," the other cunt responded, and the bunch of cunts leered over the man with the sign thinking over the transaction. "How much do you want for a slap?" one asked him, laughing like an arse farts.

We moved through the crowds and caught another train, my pink suit soaked. I chose the suit as though I were Miss Moneypenny and reached the Ribble Valley stinking of female sweat. The hotel was in walking reach, but I was so horribly exhausted Morgan told me to lie down and went and bought a single Laphroaig from the empty bar. It was the only hotel in reach and opulent in the way country hotels are opulent while still being slightly grubby and lace-sodden. I lay in my heels on a bed covered in faux fur and scanned the room. Perhaps it was what I was "used to," but certainly not what I would be used to by the end of the year with no money, no income, everything going on rent and biscuits and air freshener and electricity and the things normal people buy. I saw myself laid out on the chaise longue at the foot of the bed in an exquisite gabardine gown, smoking smack off perfect silver foil through an ornate silver tube. I saw Morgan stood by the heavily velvet-curtained windows, sleeves rolled up, wearing braces and smoking a Vogue cigarette. I saw us both shivering in the corner withdrawing with green puke all over the lustrous carpets. I saw us laid out stoned on the thick polar bear rug. I saw us black, blue, white and dead, living, sane and crazy. Every shade of who we were was in the room with me and none of them were infinite, none of them were human, or possible, or written.

We try hard to learn. Morgan has been clean the longest and has the most selective memory and is the less able of us to admit when addicted. I have to explain to Morgan on day five of drinking some elaborate liquor each night "to get to sleep" that it's a habit, and that week two will suggest an addiction, and I let Morgan make the case against potentially swapping smack for hard liquor out loud to hear what is actually being said: telling me how necessary it is and how if there's no smack there has to be *something*. Then after a two-minute pause Morgan looks depleted and says slowly... "*yeah*." But addicts are not that terrible. At least we know how to live.

*

The night at the Manor in the Ribble Valley was sleepless and slow. Morgan's breath on my neck lying in the huge bed beside me seemed to drag me through its teeth. My shoulders felt hot then cold then hard then stiff. I wound my leg around Morgan's legs then unwound it over and again. The now familiar smell of whisky and salt suffocated me. A terrible glint of light cast a single blue arrow over our bodies. I licked Morgan's shoulder to see how it tasted. I shuddered at the thought of the man at the station with the sign and the punched-in face. I winced at the thought of seeing my husband again. I imagined how he might look, whether he might appear healthy, or happy, or just as indifferent, or bald, or less indifferent. Less indifferent was far more frightening. How many years I had yearned to see less indifferent expressions and hear less indifferent thoughts or exclamations, and ne'er did they make themselves known. I thought of him as recesses of thought and opinion, each so locked into a cellar of indifference they may as well have been iron-cast and forever locked away in a forgotten crypt.

In the morning we waited in the foyer, beneath the arch of the entrance doorway, a pungent rain dazzling the otherwise subdued vista of oak trees and claggy lawn. Pussy willow in my eyeline dripped into my focus and out again. Spinning jennies all over the driveway, Mercedes and BMWs drove up with a gravelly purr then drove away. I dipped my peep-toe shoe in a puddle and out again. I wondered if I'd made enough effort to see them or not enough. I pulled a knot out of my hair and smelled my hands to ensure I'd washed the cigarette smell from them. Morgan went inside, then decided my love should be with me when my husband showed. Nothing really materialised into full consciousness, not even sound. Then the rough sound of a poorly-made German car on the listless white gravel and their faces emerging from over the dashboard where a small Hawaiian-themed air-freshener hung between the two faces. I may have gasped. Morgan stiffened and took my arm.

Four *I've Got A Secret (Didn't We Shake, Sugaree?)*

The morning is just a pale blue line that quivers a little before the pain in my bones returns to the foremost point in my consciousness and I emit sounds I have no desire to hear myself make. Morgan describes them as "wounded animal noises," wakes and gives me an arm or a leg or a hand to squeeze and I implore my love, "help me."

I wake anytime between 4am and 12pm. I sleep anytime between 2am and 6am. I nap when the morphine kicks in. We structure our lives around the boy and his three days a week with us. Six months of bartering with a newly dressed and scrubbed, unscathed ex-husband have given us a semblance of family life, or what it would be or could be, or what it might have been, but it's through a shot lens. It's through opiate pain relief and the buzzing of all our debtors closing in beyond the point of where our happiness melds with our newly acquired realism.

Sometimes I wake to Joe's kiss. A sweet kiss on the lips, and his breath whispers, "mum, wake up," a lemon-like sour taste with a metallic tang from the medicines and the sleep deprivation. Tea and Morgan, Morgan and tea and Joe shaking the house with enigmatic warblings about space-time and playing swing ball in the garden. If everything in the house has a price tag, we can't afford any of it. Hours turn like whole days used to.

*

I am unlocked. They say it's the infection, the lump, the surgery, the drug abuse, the virus I had during the last withdrawal that made me punch my own limbs, the stress, the breakdown. They say these things lay dormant in you sometimes and then decide it's the right time to test your strength. The brain doctor did the scans, the whirring light machines, the feeling that your entire head is a clock. The clock stopped and started with the slightest jolt and never set back to the same time again. They say it's a neurological illness or disorder, that my nervous system is attacking itself because it has decided there is a foreign body in my brain. The myelin sheath scarred with the war I waged against myself introvertedly. Perhaps my body is just exhausted and sick of living. I was always at war in this way but never supposed it would damage an organ. Somehow I feel damaged within, not chemically, not down to the plasma and neurons and cells, but in a more profound way I have simply always been sad.

Out in the garden our cat, Frank, chases his tail then rolls in the sickly-looking grass.

Joe retrieves his basketball with a thud-thud then his football to bash and he runs in a circle in the room where I sit with sour breath smiling and then he runs up the stairs to tell Morgan about a butterfly he saw then he rounds Frank up and swaddles him murmuring "ahh my little boy! My little baby cat!" Every sensation and thought and image seems recurring and constant, they just add up and patch over one another and create a hideous and overwhelming tapestry of existing that leaks so far beyond these walls. I fear we are the only living creatures actually thinking, feeling and seeing anything at all. A walled garden becomes a cul-de-sac in a walled, historic town inside an inverted version of Tory Britain inside a convoluted idea of existence dreamt up thousands of years ago and endorsed by rich academics. Altogether I am so apart from this world I seek to be nowhere other than where I am.

We took the house and raised the money but I'll never recall how. The kindness of friends, the hustle. Accumulating things is easy. It just takes imagination to get on in life. I've been reborn in real time several times in several episodes which feel like eras in themselves or maybe like *stints*. Most of my life has felt like sentences or stretches of time in which I was incarcerated within a situation, hoping for change. Teenage pregnancy, prostitution, drug addiction, working in an abattoir for minimum wage, domestic violence, nervous breakdowns, years of negative charge of the soul never reaching beyond a minor key. Each change arrived due to a loss of some kind. If I lost the thing that was keeping me incarcerated I could leave. There was one main jailor keeping me stuck the whole time, the umpteen stretches. I hadn't seen him since I was twenty-one and sectioned for a breakdown precipitated by large regular quantities of LSD and seeing the body of my then partner hanging from the ceiling in his flat.

My jailor's name changed several times owing to being a con-man and having houses repossessed or having to assume a false identity due to incomprehensible, repeated counts of fraud. The last time I knew him his name was Leslie.

I received word of his death in my kitchen in our new home only weeks after moving in with no furniture beside a blow-up bed that regularly deflated. My uncle Martin came by to see where I was living and how I was still alive after the stories he'd heard from my mother – all embellished or fictionalised as she had not seen me in several years but enjoyed creating paranoiac tragedies in which I was the protagonist.

Martin stooped in the kitchen while I stewed tea. I was astounded by his hairline and his aura. He seemed thinner, though not physically. I imagined that's what living a life in continuum in this one part of the world might do – a socialist all his life and now whittling away to dust before his own eyes. He could tell me little that I wanted to hear – several family members were mentioned in succession as I brushed them away like specks on my shoulder with the words, "what about?" or "remember?" and swiftly changing tack. Then he stuttered, "but you know about

Leslie?"

"Pour quoi?"

"He's dead. It only happened about a week ago."

I took not a second to reply, "Oh that is good news. I hope it was painful."

Morgan knew Leslie's shadow and how it turned over in my sleep in my bed each night without Morgan ever having met him. If you ever loved me, you knew his shadow. When Martin told me of Leslie's death I slipped into another place – lightly and with nothing more than a short cough, the world changed from splendour and poverty into a soul-mangling dark mass of colic-walloping queasy distress. Like being unliberated. Like seeing the Berlin wall reform itself in slow motion. Like eating a horse's liver and it rekindling inside your body and becoming one with your own, half chewed and not of the right species.

With terrible gratitude I met his death but the aftermath was an undeniable wave of regret at having ever had the consciousness to be able to recall the thousand nights he wanked over me as a child, or had me fellate him, or pushed his tobacco-stained fingers into my orifices so I felt like a pig or just a prolapsed organ on an autopsy table.

His death leaked into my daytime somehow, and I became torturously sick.

Nausea pills were the first treatment from the doctor. He told Morgan, not me, that I would be fine, it would be a short-term illness and would "clear up." He couldn't tell Morgan what was wrong with me and seemed to have decided all women were too retarded to understand medicine.

I had frequent blackouts. My breath would become weak then ragged and the world collapsed onto its side breathing for me. Morgan learned to sit and rub my hand as I wouldn't simply come around, but no doctor seemed particularly interested in my sudden semi-narcoleptic presentation. I had one more appointment with my old breast consultant in London and my GP told me to go. Morgan and I travelled on the train in bleakest despondency and without pain relief so that as soon as we arrived there was only one solution as we saw it with our rational minds: to score, and we were swept into the headfirst love dream once again, tar-smeared and as old as age we lay in the bed we abandoned for a trip to make a life as though a life is a structure one can make rather than simply inhabit. We chased and lay clenched and purring with the sound of rain over the skylight and our ex-landlady off her skull on cocaine laughing manically downstairs and calling up every so often as she'd not anticipated our return and hoped to cash in on the possibility that we hadn't settled and would return to claim her mortgage payments in state benefits.

There was never a moment we wanted it to end; there had not been such a moment before and it would never arise while we were in the dream-within-a-rancid-rented-attic. No cleanliness beat it. No security or liberty or wealth – there was not a hair's breadth of doubt between Morgan and I and heroin.

And Morgan smelled like Morgan only more Morgan. And I felt alive though beyond life and somewhere where the terminology attached to being alive or dead ceased to be relevant. I had come home. Every time heroin and I hook up, *I come home*.

*

You can learn to hate most things you are obsessed with. A certain taste you covet and crave all your years can turn awful in a mouthful. A voice or a sound you admire or can't get enough of can simply become unimportant or unaffecting. We knew that wasn't our fate with heroin.

The hospital appointment penetrated the day that broke with

the snuffling of two stoned lovers in a bed full of ash and sun-light as the alarm on Morgan's phone chirped until our landlady shouted up in her rude Germanic yowl. Hitting the correct button on the phone, we turned to one another and our eyes dilated a fraction more than they had in two days. There was never any time Morgan and I had to discuss a plan when we were on heroin. It invariably began with: smoke as much as you can before we go into the real world, then buy as much as you can on the way back into retreat so we can continue the dream. Anything beyond heroin was an interlude we simply had to go forth into with slight clarity and do our best.

We were gouching on the bus and I could only stay awake by wringing my hands. "I think we had too much," Morgan mum-bled a couple of times and a couple more times I insisted, "you've got to not gouch. Keep your eyes open."

Anxiety peaked in the waiting room while Morgan whispered that I was far too paranoid, we weren't holding, and after checking my eyes a dozen times, we lied to ourselves that my pupils weren't pinned. I tried to look at myself in a steel trolley as it passed and was convinced I'd have to do a piss test because I nearly always did, and although Class A drugs had been tested and recorded sev-eral times, the consultants had never mentioned it. "They don't care about that shit," Morgan mused, optimistically. "Everyone in London has some kind of Class A drug in them."

The new consultant assigned to me was a twenty-something brat with hair that looked like a sheet of black chiffon and eyes that bore into the pit of your throat. I just started talking, forget-ting why I was there. "Yeah, I've been ok. That bit," pointing at my right breast, "got better, I think. It hurts, when I'm lying on it, when you touch it; it's swollen a lot. It looks ok, I guess. I'm sick though. Everywhere else. I've been asking the doctors up there to help me. Is it this again? Am I sick there again?" I sounded like a twelve-year-old after a sustained coma. The consultant barely blinked or swallowed and time whooshed around like a bonkers procession of flies and insects and they entered her mouth and I was spitting them out and Morgan's eyes were completely blurred by them. She asked me about the surgery. I explained verbatim what the discharge note had said. She said I didn't seem to understand what had been done or what had been wrong with me. She asked if I'd endured any recent stress. I began to cry; in fact, it was more of a dull howl with rising sniffles and choking throbbing notes of clarity.

"Do you know why you were having breast care for....eight months?"

Morgan squeezed my hand and spoke for me whenever necessary. "She's tired. She's travelled a long way. She's been unwell."

"Do you feel unwell... Florence?"

"I feel so unwell! Oh God I'm sick!"

Morgan tried to dissuade the doctor from asking more questions. When I couldn't speak for sobbing, she transferred me to the bed to show her my radiant red breast scar. She touched, poked, squeezed and rubbed while I choked on my own saliva and snot and, looking extremely aggrieved, left the room to get the surgeon who had operated on me. I heard them speaking outside and Morgan shushed me to listen. "Chronic drug abuse. Yes. We found heroin in her system the day of surgery. We had to operate. Her body wouldn't fight the infection. Are there any lumps? Yes, we thought inflammatory breast cancer at the time. No, she's still using. Yes, smoking too."

With one inhalation of stale air I blacked out and came round with Morgan's hand rubbing mine and a nurse taking my blood pressure and pulse. Everyone seemed friendlier, even the consultant. Morgan was trying to explain why we'd come to London and why hadn't we gone to A&E in the north if I was having episodes like that. Neither of us could answer any questions and the consultant shimmied around the drugs issue that was now laid out on the table. I needed a fix and when she told us to go to A&E and that she'd have someone get a wheelchair we both made our garbled and hesitant excuses. "Do you understand you're unwell and need help?" she asked. I didn't reply but began to cry again. "Your blood pressure is too high, I think you need to be seen."

"I've been seen. I've been felt up by so many doctors I feel like a prostitute!" I yelled. "I can't do this being ill thing anymore. I don't know the protocol! I don't know what this being ill is about! You go here then there then you get sicker and if you're not sick enough this person won't see you and if you're too sick then you can't even get out of bed to go see anyone!"

I felt the street sweep me up as we left Homerton clutching our belongings and watching vigilantly as though some terrible beast was about to turn a corner into the street and hurry us to our deaths. Morgan told me not to cry and I staggered pitifully. The bus ride was sinful and overheated and I swayed in the aisle, doped and troubled. Alighting at Stamford Hill we gasped our way through the onslaught of passengers and into the street where, in a flutter of lost momentum, I collapsed.

*

What else is there for suffering so wild?

An inner entrancement had rooted in my heart as I hit the pavement. Wordless, we chased what felt like a gallon of smack and struggled to keep track of the bags, mistakenly deciding we'd lost one under the bed or inside our own clothes. Morgan was petrified and shaking. I'd cut my head on the stairs on the way up to the attic after Morgan roused me to consciousness several times on the way back to the old house. Apparently strangers had been offering to help but Morgan was determined to hold me up and we stumbled on. The moment my eyes became alert again I needed a fix. We reminded each other we weren't addicted again yet – another day and we would be. The hours became very cruel and my heart yammered through the night as I vomited, smoked, passed out and chased. Each time my heart settled it zoomed again, pattering and yelping until I lost my sight.

"We can't do this anymore," Morgan said as the tea and sugar ran out and the light began to apply its vivid mosquito netting over our room in a perfectly blue hour. Morgan's eyeballs looked grey in a blue face pickled in smoke. A vein flashed a warning in my love's tense forehead and I petered around the edges of the morning, feeling less astonished by unconsciousness than consciousness. We were blighted to ever return, feeling.

*

I wrote a letter to heroin to try to say goodbye.

Dear Heroin,

The day we left you I could only do it if I knew we could have you back. I know you're out there in the world somewhere else making other people feel better and one day we'll find you. It might be soon. This bullshit pharmacy morphine is nothing on you. Such a clean feeling and no high. If only it came in powdered form I could attempt to replicate what you do, but they don't love you like we do; and they don't understand that you would make all this ok.

One night when we were together I was wearing nothing but a linen shirt which felt like the most exquisite garment, and we lit candles to not have to flick the lighter every few seconds, and I remember telling you that all these things we try so hard to find out, and know, about the universe, and time, and space, and truth – I remember saying to you that I finally understood that we're simply not supposed to know. I never had a purer thought in all my life. Everything pushed right out to the reaches of my own known existence and I heard myself breathe and felt myself cry. I pushed my fingertips into the candle flame and burned them and sucked them and let the breeze from the open window cool my flushed chest and cheeks and I thought about all the people I thought I loved and all the things I thought I wanted and knew if I died right then I'd die in a kind of singular happiness no other creature had ever felt so entirely but me.

Five *I'd Rather Go Blind*

The wheelchair arrived with the word "KARMA" emblazoned in white with two cherubic wings over the R. Morgan saw the past and all futility. I pondered over the sinister aspect of karma, and why anyone would choose it for a person with a disability. "You can't push me in that thing," I told Morgan, who paled over and found a reason to leave the room.

I thought often about sin and whether I had committed any great sins in my life. I'd committed perhaps nuanced sins, if such things existed in modern consciousness. Drugs, some petty theft, lies to support the drugs and petty theft. I had allowed my husband to have a quiet affair to avoid confronting the catastrophe and the direction it pointed towards. I had toyed with beliefs without ever truly having any. I had fallen in love and invited Morgan to love me for life and my life was now seeming so feint as to invite guilt that even the love of my life perhaps wouldn't have me for long. As though any decision we make or any action we apply volition to makes any difference to the lie of the land when you're looking at the knots and rivulets and scarring in the map of What Was. Nothing follows the other thing. Linearity is an illusion, a tether. We rivet ourselves to it so as to imagine propulsion to a territory we made through good choices and pure notions of futures and forward motions; my mother with her sleeping mouth revealing the cursed teeth from her years of smoking cigarettes then denying it for decades. If she keeps her lips curled and smoothed around them no one knows. We spend most of our years papering over things we'd rather not see.

I surrender these ideas as falsehoods and go about my days plucking all pretty things from my imagination and stewing them in a great big vat of relief.

There are evenings when Joe falls asleep on Morgan's shoulder on the sofa watching a film and I sit and sip milk or tea and feel personally blessed to be a witness to something so banal and lovely. Time stops around them, they look like two angels caught in a snow globe with charity shop furniture and warm and bobbled second-hand clothes.